Your Breaking Point

Effective steps to reduce and cope with stress

by

Dolores Whelan

Attic Press
Dublin

First published in Ireland in 1993 by
Attic Press
4 Upper Mount Street
Dublin 2

British Library Cataloguing in Publication Data

Whelan, Dolores
Your Breaking Point: Effective steps to reduce and cope with stress
I. Title
155.9

ISBN 1-85594-071-X

Cover Design: Van Hara Design
Origination: Verbatim Typesetting & Design
Printing: Guernsey Press Ltd

Acknowledgements

I would like to thank: Attic Press my publishers for inviting me to write this book, and Dolores McGill for typing the manuscript; John Quinn in RTE radio for his support of my work over the years; my many teachers in the USA and Ireland who offered me such wide vision and possibilities; the Creation Spirituality Network in Ireland and England for many exciting events; all the wonderful people who have been part of the Iomlánú network over the past seven years; my parents Gerald and Carmel Whelan and all my family for constantly supporting my vision; Neil McCann, my husband, partner and dear friend for his love and support and the wonderful vision we share.

Dedication

This book is dedicated to all those who are searching for a gentler and less stressful way to live on this beautiful planet.

About the author

Dolores Whelan is an educator and group facilitator. Her qualifications include an M.Sc. in Biochemistry from TCD and an M.A. in Spirituality. She is a massaage therapist and has training in psychosynthesis. She founded the Iomlánú centre for Healing and Creative Living in Dundalk in 1986. She is a frequent contributor in RTE radio programmes, including the recent series on stress management, *Mind How You Go.*

Contents

Introduction

We live in times of great uncertainty and huge change as we approach the end of the twentieth century. Change has always characterised life on this planet – but the types and rate of change being experienced at this time are great and disturbing for many. The certainties we took for granted in the past no longer seem so sure. Through the media we see evidence of breakdown of many of the institutions we assumed were unshakeable. We are constantly bombarded with world news, much of it distressing – as we hear of wars, famines, drought and the ozone depletion, nuclear waste and oil spills. All of this greatly impinges on our own peace of mind to cause disquiet at conscious and unconscious levels.

There has been much change over the past few centuries – some of which has been good. One of the consequences of the progress has been the speeding up of the pace of life to a level never before experienced. As a consequence of this increased pace at which we live, and the excessively narrow focus of people's lives, we are very much out of touch with our own nature and our true selves. We, in the western world, live in a society that does not honour the seasonal nature of life with its cycles of growth and decline, death and rebirth. Society often only measures achievement in terms of an end product, values only the material aspect of reality and defines success and happiness in terms of possessions.

We no longer value the intangible aspects of life and community. We constantly strive for happiness outside ourselves, often consuming endlessly to fill the emptiness. This imbalance can lead to people feeling cut off from their real nature and causes much unhappiness and distress. To be a whole person we need to be in touch with all aspects of our being – body, mind, emotions and spirit. Health and wholeness are closely connected – the more I am in touch with all of myself the healthier I will be. Emotions buried and undealt with cause much physical and mental disease.

Many of the diseases in our world are stress-related and have their origin in the non-physical. Yet most of the methods developed to deal with these illnesses reflect the materialistic mind set of our society. Modern medicine, while excellent in many aspects, also has severe limitations due to its tendency to deal almost exclusively with symptoms rather than to probe for root causes. Illness is often treated in isolation from the person and their life circumstances, physical, emotional and social. Much evidence has accumulated to show that the body and mind affect and influence the health and well-being of each other. While some medical practitioners accept this, the acceptance needs to be more widespread.

Giving workshops and lectures to many different groups of people, I have become aware of another source of distress in people's lives – lack of self-acceptance. I have been amazed by the amount of unhappiness experienced by people partly due to their inability to love and accept themselves. One of the consequences of not loving yourself is that you may not take care of yourself. In particular, women in our society have been encouraged to be selfless, always to put other people and their needs before their own. This leads to a great imbalance and doesn't really serve anyone in the long term. Often I meet people who are overburdened with their sense of responsibility for others. Many of these people have lost the vitality and joy of living and constantly feel depressed and unhappy. When vitality and joy are lacking, it is difficult for us to respond to the joys, sorrows and challenges that each day brings. All of these issues cause us as a society to experience stress and distress and the associated illnesses that result.

I believe that as individuals and as a society we need to

get back in touch with the essence of who we are and what our lives are about. To do this we need to stop the noise — internal and external — that constantly distracts us and keeps us out of touch with our true selves.

I hope this book and the reflections and exercises contained in it will be a useful tool for you as you allow yourself the time and the space to question who you are, where you are at, and where you wish to go.

Dolores Whelan
August 1993

Chapter 1

Stress and distress

Stress has only recently become a topic of conversation in the lives of ordinary people. Stress (in its present form) has not always been a part of our lives: when people speak of stress today they are rarely referring to the natural tensions that give us an edge in life – give us the energy to get a task finished – within a certain time frame, or the edge that makes life exciting without being exhausting.

Life and the art of living constantly require a balancing between two opposite poles; in the case of stress, between relaxation and tension. If one finds oneself in a permanent state of either tension or relaxation one will not be able to live and function in the world. Being in a state of balance does not mean that a person achieves a balance once and then preserves it throughout life – since human beings are living things, they and their systems are in a state of constant change. Responding to changes, internal and external, finding new places of balance is a key aspect in the art of living successfully.

Stress is medically defined as the body's response to any change – good or bad. Stress can be experienced by us when we are the recipients of good news or of bad news, when good and exciting events or difficult and depressing events happen to us. Stress is a necessary part of our lives and we don't want to eliminate it. A certain amount of tension is necessary in order to perform the tasks of daily life. Our bodies are well equipped to deal with stress up to a certain point. What allows the body to manage the stresses of living is having the periods of tension interspersed with periods of relaxation. Frequent short periods of relaxation allow the body to release the tension that has accumulated making it ready to cope with the next set of stresses, strains and tensions.

Stress is a term used to describe a general state of being. It is clarifying the to distinguish between different types of stress. Stress is neutral until it strikes its target, when it can be experienced as either a positive challenge or as a negative problem.

Stress and relaxation

When stress is experienced as a positive challenge it can bring out the very best in that person and in that situation. When stress is experienced as a problem and is seen as negative it can bring out the worst in a person. Positive stress is often called 'eustress' while negative stress is called 'distress'. Both require certain levels of tension and both need to be balanced by periods of relaxation. So what is relaxation? Relaxation is not something we do, it is something that happens when we let go of tension. Relaxation is learning to recognise and reduce unnecessary and accumulated tension so as to enhance our well-being and increase our effectiveness. Learning ways of releasing tension is very important and central to our capacity to handle stress so that it works for us rather than against us. Stress, whether of the positive or negative type, if not balanced with relaxation will lead in time to physical, emotional and mental suffering eventually causing illness and burn-out. Much of the illness that plagues people at the end of the twentieth century is due to stress and distress often unrecognised and mismanaged.

Feeling out of control

In order to live rather than just survive in our present society, each of us needs a balance in our lives. We need a mixture of challenge, relaxation, exercise, good air, proper nutrition, rest, personal support, a sense of purpose and fun. When several of these ingredients are missing or in short supply we can feel overwhelmed and saddened,

14

frustrated and burnt-out. Many people whose lives are negatively affected by stress share the experience of feeling out of control of the circumstance of their lives. This then adds to their experience of distress.

The body is very well equipped to deal with stress under certain circumstances and up to a certain limit. The body has two distinct responses to the stress it encounters: the ancient and autonomic primary stress response and the more recent and more complex secondary stress response.

Stress responses

The primary stress response was learned by humans millions of years ago when, as a species we roamed the wild and needed to be able to respond with action at the slightest hint of danger, since our survival depended on it. This primary stress response is automatic and is the same in all people. Often called the 'fight or flight response', this was developed at a time when the appropriate responses to the stresses experienced involved either fleeing for safety or staying to fight and protect. This primary and automatic response is still an active part of our human coping mechanism, even though the physical circumstances of our lives and the stress experienced by us rarely requires us to 'fight' or 'flee' in the same way as our ancestors did. Because this is so, the very response originally created for our survival can in our present circumstances work against us and cause us harm.

So what happens when we experience danger or threat? When someone experiences an event that is perceived as threatening or potentially dangerous the primary stress response is triggered in the body by the action of the Hypothalmus (a small group of cells located at the base of the brain). The body, its organs and systems are put onto red alert and a complex series of chemical and physiological reactions result. A simple outline of these events is presented in the following table.

Table of events – How we physically react to threatening situations:

Table A

Organ/system	What it does during arousal	What happens in the body	Under continued stress
Adrenal glands	Produce cortisol	Convert liver glycogen to blood sugar to provide instant energy	Mobilise fat and protein stored in liver to produce more energy
Lungs	Increase breathing rate in the top lobes of lungs	Breathing becomes shallow and faster (panting)	Over-breathing continues and worsens
Heart/ cardiovascular system	Releases adrenaline (steroids) and nor-adrenaline into the blood-stream	Speeds up all the energy systems in the body. Heart rate increases. Blood flow increases. Clotting increases. Oxygen intake increases and is carried faster to the cells	Heart rate, blood pressure increase, heart overworks. Irregular heartbeat, blood more likely to clot
Digestive tract	Processes shut down	Blood diverted away from the digestive system	Acid secreted, digestion slowed, leads to ulcers
Skin	Sweating increases	Body cools due to sweating	Sweating continues, loss of body fluids
Bladder and rectum	Muscles relax		Elimination process is put on hold
Muscles	Muscles tense		Muscles primed and tensed for activity

Other activities such as the sex drive are switiched off. Kidneys stop functioning properly. The immune system, the body's defence against invasion, is severely depressed, leaving us more susceptible to infection and disease.

When the primary stress response is evoked and completed the following sequence of events occur:

Figure 1 — Outline of sequence of events
Primary Stress Response

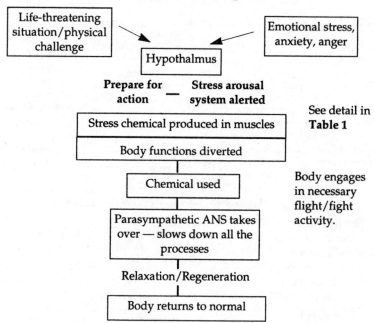

Very often stresses that are presented to us today in the forms of work pressures and social pressures cannot be responded to by the fight or flight mechanism. It is not generally socially acceptable to jump out of your car and punch the person in the car in front if you are annoyed by their driving, even if this is what your body is prepared for. So, under these circumstances this sequence will not be completed and your body will not return to a normal resting position.

The brain does not distinguish between real physical threats or dangers and those which result from anxiety and negative emotional states and when these are presented it still offers us this primary stress response as a way of coping. What happens is:

Figure 2— Outline of sequence of events

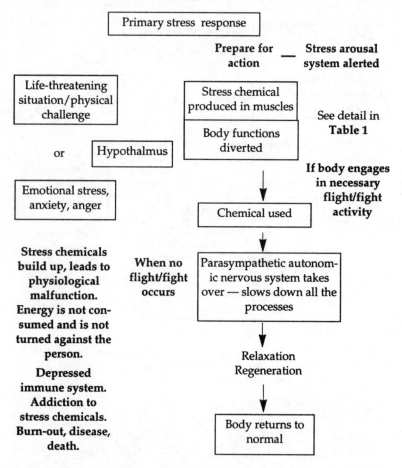

So, what can we do about this — are we powerless against this ancient system? Absolutely not! What we need to learn is to adapt this system so that it serves us well rather than exhausts and damages us. We need to learn how to switch off this response in situations where using it harms us or we need to use up the energy produced by it to bring our system back to rest.

Learning to switch off

How can we switch it off? One of the most effective and simple ways to break the cycle is through breathing. Deep slow breathing informs the Hypothalmus and switches the autonomic nervous system from the arousal response to the relaxation response and stops the sequence at the beginning. Switching from fast shallow breathing, to slow deep breathing, is a very valuable and inexpensive tool for coping with stress.

The primary stress response can also be triggered by negative thoughts, emotions and anxieties. When this is the case the cycle can be interrupted by challenging a thought pattern or belief. This will be discussed more fully in the following section on secondary stress response.

Secondary stress response

The secondary stress response is less ancient and less autonomic and much more complex than the primary stress response. It is different in its manifestation in different people. It has two aspects – the emotional (our feelings) and the cognitive (our thoughts); these aspects are controlled by different parts of the brain. The emotional aspect is stimulated by the emotional centre in the brain. It is similar in effect to the primary stress response and is usually associated with states of distress. Cognitive stress operates on a different mechanism and is activated by the frontal lobes of the thinking brain – it engages the centre of will and in general is a positive influence. If it is allowed to operate for excessive periods of time where there is no break in the stimulation and no period of relaxation to allow the system to balance itself, then an element of emotional stress is introduced. This tips the system into stress overload leading to distress.

Stress development profile

Any person who suffers from stress, emotional or cognitive, which is continuous and is not tempered with periods of relaxation, fun, exercises, or with methods of de-stressing and proper nutrients, coupled with personal support, will end up burnt-out and sick. Stress, like any other process, develops along observable patterns and has definable stages and observable symptoms. Unfortunately, one of the strange quirks of the stress syndrome is that the more stressed one becomes the less able one is to observe its effects on oneself. The stress development profile is outlined in three distinct phases, each with its own causes and its own symptoms. The profile is progressive, in that if corrective action is not taken at one stage then the stress progresses to the next phase with the ensuing symptoms and consequences.

See Table B for the three phases and symptoms and how to redress them.

Stress — Who gets it?

Since everyone is exposed to the changing dynamics of living, everyone is susceptible to stress and to distress. Stress used to be considered the executive disease – but research has shown this to be untrue. Stress, as we have seen, can be caused not only by physical challenges, but also by negative emotional states including fear, anger, shame, guilt, grief and sadness, especially when these emotions are not recognised or not expressed in a healthy way. Stress can be caused by a lack of a realistic vision of who we are and where we are and by a lack of self-esteem or self-respect. Stress (or distress) is not confined to high-powered executives but is experienced by any of the following people:

- those who may feel undervalued
- those who are stuck in a rut
- those who are unemployed
- those who are pressurised beyond their capacity
- those who are trapped in difficult life circumstances
- those who experience no sense of satisfaction or challenge in their lives.

Table B: Stress development profile

	When it occurs	Signs and symptoms	Action needed to prevent development to next stage
Phase 1: Gathering energy for special events	When extra energy is needed for special short-term projects	All our activities and behaviour are speeded up, thinking, talking, eating.	Periods of relaxation, exercise, good nutrition. Plenty of short breaks — quick relaxation techniques.
Phase II: Pushing your energy. Continuous stream of special events.	When you are living for an extended period of time at an above-normal pace — placing excess demands on yourself	You feel tense most of the time, feel, pressured, overwhelmed by schedules. Sleep is difficult. Your eating patterns change. Alcohol consumption increases. Head-aches, digestion problems, you feel driven, very irritable	Realise that you have been pushing yourself too hard and that you are not performing the way you wish to. STOP, REST, take some time to reassess schedules. Find suitable forms of relaxation to help rebalance and restore your system.
Phase III: You have blown it phase	When you don't pay attention to the signs your body gives you. When you allow yourself to keep going to the point of exhaustion.	Your energy is completely depleted— all you zest for life is gone — you can't enjoy anything, can't laugh, everything is a drag! You feel emotionally numbed. Head-aches, ulcers, heartburn, chest pains	Stop everything. Either you rest or you kill yourself. Often 1 or 2 week's rest is needed before you can even consider a suitable programme for relaxation and new work schedules.

One of the major causes of any kind of stress is the belief that one has no control over the circumstances causing the distress.

Another major contributor to a person's stress load is one's personality type. There are three personality types: Type A, Type B and Type C. Table C (over) describes the characteristics of each. It is rarely found that a person is exclusively one type or displays characteristics that are all of the same type. People are most likely to be a mixture of types with a tendency towards one or another.

Table C: Personality types and their characteristics

Type A	Type B	Type C
Very competitive	Not competitive at work or at play	Over-achievers
Strong, forceful personality	Has an easy-going manner	Hyperactive in a quiet, non-obvious way
Does everything quickly	Goes about thing slowly and methodically	Plodder
Ambitious	Not overly ambitious	Stoic
Strives for promotion at work or for social advancement	Is fairly content with present position at work and socially	Dependable
Wants public recognition for their efforts	Has no desire for public recognition	Cheerful
Is easily angered by people and events	Slow to be aroused to anger	Seems always to be able to cope
Feels restless when inactive	Enjoys periods of idleness	Never gives in to illness/fatigue
Speaks quickly	Speaks slowly	Finds it difficult to say no to excessive demands
Thrives on doing several things at the same time	Is more content when doing things one at a time	Perfectionist
Walks, moves and eats quickly	Is unhurried in walking moving and eating	Driven by fear of failure
Very impatient	Patient and not upset by delay	Very high expectations of self
Extremely conscious of time — revels in having to meet deadlines	Not time-conscious ignores deadlines	Difficulty in expressing feelings — especially negative ones
Always arrives on time	Is often late	Difficulty in assessing personal limitations
		Difficulty in admitting vulnerability

Types A and C are much more prone to distress and mismanaged stress while Type B is likely to avoid excess stress. While each person comes into this world with certain characteristics and tendencies, much of our adult behaviour is learned and therefore it can be unlearned or changed. Nobody was born exclusively or irredeemably Type A, B or C. So when you look at the table and locate yourself within a certain type there is no need to feel that 'that is it' – there is nothing you can do about this.

Recognising relaxation

Relaxation is the opposite part of the dynamic in the stress equation. But what does it look like? What are the signs and symptoms of relaxation? We are all familiar with the signs and symptoms of tension and arousal, more so than with those of relaxation. There are many observable signs – some of which you will be familiar with. Here is a list of symptoms associated with the relaxed state.

- Slower breathing
- Deeper breathing
- Easier breathing
- Breathing with the belly
- Sense of openness
- Sense of connectedness
- Sense of calmness
- Sense of peacefulness
- Flow of feelings
- Muscles softening
- Body feeling heavier and warmer
- A feeling of lightness within yourself

What other symptoms can you add to your personal list?
-
-
-
-
-

What causes stress?

Anything can cause us to experience stress. That which does so is called a 'stressor'. Stressors can be broadly classified in origin as follows:

- Environmental
- Chemical
- Work
- Emotional
- Family/relationships
- Financial

Environmental stressors

Since we interact constantly with, and are affected by, our environment (the space or place around us), it is important that we can identify things in our environment which cause us distress. The impact of the environment on our stress levels will be quite different depending on whether we live in a crowded city or a small rural town or in the country. City traffic jams, crowded buses and trains and the noise and pollution associated with city life are serious causes of stress. Overcrowding, inadequate housing, or workplaces, lack of proper lighting, heating and ventilation also contribute to environmental stress. Excessive noise, even when we block it out, unconsciously triggers the stress response of the autonomic nervous system and causes us distress.

Chemical stressors

Chemical stressors are of two types: one is due to chemicals which are present as pollutants in the air or water system. The second is due to chemicals present in the food and drinks that we consume. Caffeine, sugar, alcohol and salt are chemicals which are stressful for the body. Very often stress provoking foods are the ones we turn to during stressful times. So, we may drink more coffee or tea, or eat cream buns or chocolate when stressed.

Work stressors

For many people, work and the workplace is a great source

of stress. People experience stress in the workplace for many different reasons. For some, too much pressure, for others, too little challenge. Some people set themselves and others deadlines which are unrealistic; others experience stress due to unclear definitions of responsibility; for others it is a lack of support on the job; and for many it is the inability to handle conflictional relationships in the workplace.

At different times one may experience stress from several different categories. When they are allowed to continue without some action being taken, they lead to a variety of different results – some of these are outlined in the next section.

Family and relational stressors
Much of the stress in our lives comes from bad communications. Unresolved conflicts and our difficulties in relating to people close to us are big causes of stress. Difficulties between spouses, children or parents are among the common sources of stress that we encounter.

Financial stressors
Money, a lack of it, too much of it, what to do with or without it, all of these can be causes of stress in our lives. So, not having enough money to pay for rent, or having a million pounds from the Lotto – both are stressful.

Emotional stressors
Until recently it was not understood how negative emotions, such as fear, guilt, shame, anxiety, grief bereavement and low self-esteem affected us. It has been clearly shown that these factors add considerably to the stress loading. Facing or thinking about a fearful situation, feeling guilt about a proposed act or a past one, can be stressful.

Cognitive stressors
Thinking patterns affect us perhaps more than we imagine. Inflexible attitudes, rigidity of thinking and fear of change all contribute to our stress load.

EFFECTS OF STRESS?

When stress is unattended to and unheeded it causes problems; these include difficulties in many areas of our lives and ripple out to cause problems in society or within an organisation.

Emotional effects

The emotions or expressions of emotions which one may experience as a direct result of feeling stressed can be listed. You may encounter only one of the emotions on the list. Generally, you will experience a combination of all of them to a lesser extent.

The key emotional effects of stress are as follows:

- Anxiety
- Aggression
- Apathy
- Boredom
- Depression
- Fatigue
- Frustration
- Guilt
- Shame
- Irritability
- Bad temper
- Moodiness
- Low self-esteem
- Threat
- Tension
- Nervousness
- Loneliness

Behavioural effects

Being stressed can lead to all sorts of unusual or even dangerous behaviour including:

- Accident proneness
- Drug taking

- Emotional outbursts
- Excessive eating
- Loss of appetite
- Excessive drinking
- Smoking
- Excitability
- Impulsive behaviour
- Impaired speech
- Nervous laughter
- Restlessness
- Trembling

Health effects

Again, if you are stressed, you may experience one or all or a combination of these:

- Asthma
- Amenorrhoea
- Chest and back pains
- Coronary heart disease
- Diarrhoea
- Faintness and dizziness
- Dyspepsia
- Frequent urination
- Headaches and migraine
- Neuroses, nightmares
- Insomnia, psychoses
- Psychosomatic disorder
- Diabetes mellitus
- Skin rash
- Ulcers
- Loss of sexual interest

Long-term stressed people can develop quite serious disabilities and ill health if the stress is not tackled or lessened.

Cognitive effects

Cognitive effects are the effects of stressors on our ability to think and carry out mental tasks. They may include:

- Inability to make decisions and concentrate
- Frequent forgetfulness
- Hypersensitivity to criticism
- Mental blocks

Stress overload also severely inhibits our capacity to relate to and communicate with other people. This, of course, leads to frustration, conflict and bad relationships within the home, family, partnerships and workplace. This in turn leads to much wasted energy and unhappiness in social circles. It can cause a person to feel they have reached breaking point.

Organisational effects

The personal effects of stress spill over into the wider world. In the workplace it leads to:

- Absenteeism
- Poor industrial relations
- Poor productivity
- High accident and labour turnover rates
- Poor organisational climate
- Antagonism at work
- Job dissatisfaction

The effects of stress are widespread and pervasive. Therefore, it is of utmost importance that each of us knows and understands not only how stress and distress works in a general way, but how our stresses affect us personally and how we can manage them more efficiently, so that we meet the challenges of life in a healthy and life-giving way.

In the next chapter we will discuss and explore stress and its effects at a more personal level, offering you an opportunity to explore your own stress profile and suggesting ways to reduce this to a level where the stress works to enhance, rather than to destroy your life.

Chapter 2

Stress and you

Stress is a neutral force until it strikes its target. Whether the complex mixture of stresses experienced by people leads to a positive or negative outcome depends to a large extent on the way each person responds. For some people stress evokes a positive response leading to a challenging exciting and satisfying life, for others the same stresses lead to a depressing, distressful and basically unsatisfying life.

In the last chapter we outlined various types of stressors that can impinge on us and our lives and how different stressors can influence each other and increase the overall stress level. When we find ourselves in a situation of excessive stress or distress we are faced with two major options as to how to deal with this. One option is to ignore the initial signs that tell us something is wrong and try to continue as usual or even to engage in behaviour that increases the stress. This will lead us into stress overload which sets up a whole series of dynamics leading to a predictable outcome. It will involve certain consequences at behavioural, physiological, emotional and cognitive levels (see Chapter 1 for a detailed description). If the situation is further ignored, then the short-term consequences will lead to more serious and fixed results, which may profoundly affect the way our lives are lived. The outcome of such a choice is usually negative, which adds to our stress levels and so results in repeating the vicious cycle of events. This is outlined in the diagram over.

Table D:
Stress response
Spiral A: Life depressing response

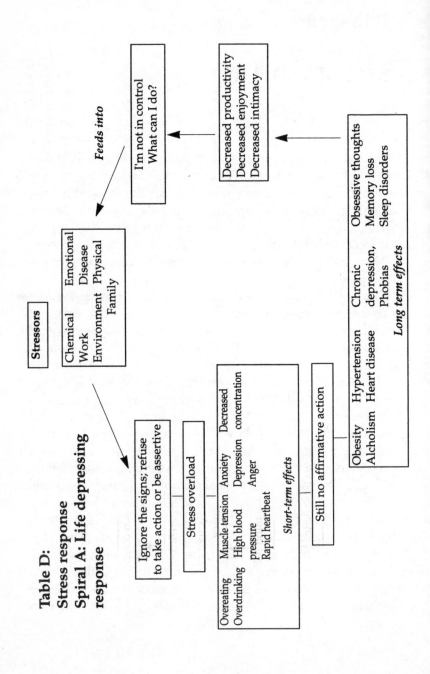

Feeds into

I'm not in control
What can I do?

Decreased productivity
Decreased enjoyment
Decreased intimacy

Stressors

Chemical   Emotional
Work   Disease   Physical
Environment
Family

Obsessive thoughts
Memory loss
Sleep disorders

Hypertension   Chronic
depression,
Phobias
Heart disease
Long term effects

Obesity
Alcholism

Ignore the signs; refuse
to take action or be assertive

Stress overload

Anxiety   Decreased
concentration
Muscle tension   Depression
High blood   Anger
pressure
Rapid heartbeat
Short-term effects

Still no affirmative action

Overeating
Overdrinking

Table E:
Stress response
Spiral B: Lifegiving response

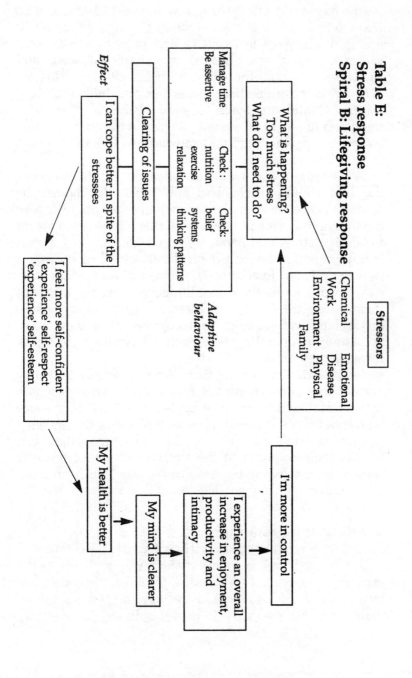

The second option leads us to an entirely different spiral of events (see Table D). If we follow the second option then we stop and take notice when things begin to get too much for us. We engage in assertive and proactive behaviour. We take care of our physical and emotional needs and challenge unhelpful thoughts and belief patterns. This not only helps the immediate issues but also builds up self-esteem. Confidence leads to good health, a clear, calm mind and finally to an overall increase in the quality of life, enjoyment, productivity and satisfaction. This can be seen as a positive spiral.

So, what is it that would cause some people to choose the first coping mechanism and others to choose the second? There are many reasons why people might choose the first option. One is a belief that this is how life is meant to be; that stress and panic are inevitable. Another reason is not knowing how to get off the treadmill or the spiral (where do I start to end this?). A major reason is that often people don't know their own limits; they are not aware of their strengths and weaknesses. They don't know themselves well enough to recognise what they need. Sometimes people don't believe they have the right to ask for what they need.

People who choose the first response believe that they are not in control or cannot take control. This itself is a major factor which increases one's stress load. For people who believe this, it is important to realise that the first step toward self-determination is the belief that they can control their response to the stressful events of life. We need to realise that to be in control of our lives is an inner dynamic and it can be developed, no matter what the external circumstances are!

Reacting or responding?

Information can lead to knowledge. Knowledge can lead to understanding and awareness which in turn leads to the capacity to choose. This capacity to make choices and to take control of situations is a key in the successful management of stress and in the art of living. The capacity to make choices allows us to move from being a victim of life's circumstances to being an empowered person. Such a person interacts with life's circumstances, both personal and social, and chooses the most appropriate response each time. People who perceive themselves as victims of events in life often react to these events rather than responding to them. If we look at the concept of reaction we see that we re-act the same way as we perhaps did last year or ten years ago (like re-running a tape). Whereas to respond is to take a new situation and be with it in all the circumstances present in this moment and then to choose a response.

Reaction implies a lack of choice and often comes from a lack of self-knowledge. A lack of accurate self-knowledge and an unwillingness to reconstruct a more realistic/honest self-image is a widespread phenomenon and is found in people of all classes, age groups and sexes. Very often people who seem to have all the prerequisites for success in life, fail to achieve what they desire – in many cases this failure can be attributed to a lack of accurate self-knowledge.

One of the great barriers to accurate self-knowledge is a tendency to judge and criticise when we notice in ourselves certain unpleasant and unacceptable traits or characteristics. Something that I have grown to realise is that criticism and judgement interfere with learning and growth, while observation and acceptance enhance it. What is essential is for each person to begin to move away from that dynamic of criticism and judgement and adopt a disposition (toward yourself) of observation and acceptance. One needs to approach self-knowledge in the way an observer approaches a subject being studied, in a spirit of openness and acceptance of what is presented. Remember, just as criticism and judgement of ourselves by other people can be negative and damaging — so too is the criticism and judgement of ourselves from within.

How well do you know yourself and your stress levels?

The following exercises are to help you get to know

yourself better, and to recognise your stress levels.

Exercise 1

Which of the following symptoms of excessive stress/
distress do you experience at the present? What kind of
physical changes do you notice when you are under
stress?
- Do you notice your chest getting tight?
- Do you notice your stomach getting tight?
- Do you notice your hands getting sweaty?
- Do you notice tension in the back of your neck?
- Do you notice your head getting tight and tense?
- Do you notice the calves of your legs getting tense?
- Do you notice your mouth getting dry?

What other kinds of physical symptoms of stress can
you list?
What kind of behavioural changes do you notice when
you are under stress?
- Do you become more irritable?
- Do you fly off the handle easily?
- Do you become more intolerant?
- Do you become anxious?
- Do you become depressed?

Are there certain events that elicit these experiences
more than others?

Exercise 2

Take a moment and reflect on these questions:

- Who am I?
- How would I describe myself to myself?

For one minute write down any words that come to
your mind. (Be careful — don't censor yourself!)

Take some time to think about the words you have
written in a detached, observational way.

Do these words evoke any strong feelings in you? Just
notice without judgement, if any feelings are evoked,
record them.

Exercise 3

Self assessment — twenty questions.
Complete as many of the following statements as possible,
or as are appropriate for you.
(You may answer them in any order you wish.)

1. One thing I like about myself is:_____
_____
_____

2. One thing I don't like about myself is:_____
_____
_____

3. Something I do very well is:_____
_____
_____

4. Something I don't do very well is:_____
_____
_____

5. A recent problem I've handled appropriately is:_____
_____
_____

6. A recent problem I have handled inappropriately is:____
_____
_____

7. A value that I aspire to practise is:_____
_____
_____

8. An example of my caring about others is:_____
_____
_____

9. People can count on me to:_____
_____
_____

10. Something I'm dealing with better this year than last
year is:_____
_____
_____

11. Something I'm dealing with worse this year than last year is:_____

_____

12. One difficulty that I have overcome is:_____

_____

_____

13. I'm best with people when:_____

_____

_____

14. I'm worst with people when:_____

_____

_____

15. I pleasantly surprised myself when I:_____

_____

_____

16. I shocked myself when I:_____

_____

_____

17. I think that I have the guts to:_____

_____

_____

18. I don't think that I have the guts to:_____

_____

_____

19. One way in which I am very dependable is:_____

_____

_____

20. One way in which I am not very dependable is:_____

_____

_____

An important aspect of self-knowledge is to know what the issues are and to be aware of the things that drain your energy and your zest for life, and to know also what things give you energy or give you a lift.

When asked at a workshop a group of people spoke about what drained their energy and what gave them energy. They came up with the following; a list of energy drains and a list of energy sources.

Energy drains

Lack of time	Envy
Lack of money	Sorrow
Lack of co-operation	Grief
Lack of humour	Loneliness
Lack of love	Conflicts in relationships
Loss of a sense of self	Failure in relationships
Lack of exercise	Lack of mental organisation
Lack of play	Feeling responsible
Lack of privacy	Feeling stupid
Loss of inner harmony	Obsessions
Noise	Fear and anxiety
Disorder	Self-punishment
Hunger	Guilt
Mismanagement	Unfulfilled dreams
Illness	Inability to forgive
Crowds	An uncreative atmosphere
Too many demands	Pessimism
Stereo blaring	Preoccupation with mistakes
Driving in heavy traffic	Depression

Confusion	Poor communication
Misunderstanding	Feeling let down by others
Hatred	Sense of meaninglessness
Anger	Lack of intimacy
Jealousy	Public apathy

Energy sources

✓ Walking through woods	Achieving an aim
Visiting an art museum	Good health
Going to the zoo	Good nutrition
Working in my garden	A good cry
Painting a picture	Dinner 'out'
Knitting	Co-operation
✓ Good friends	Activity with a friend
Silence (peace and quiet)	Competition
✓ Dancing	Having a good argument
A good book	Doing something courageous
A holiday	A good night's sleep
✓ Communion with God	Sharing laughter
The support of others	Being complemented
Acceptance of others	Singing
Getting a hug	Feeling centred
A neat office or room	Seeing a meaning in my life
Organised surroundings	Doing physical exercise
Sufficient money	Going to a sports event
A nature walk	Somebody asking my advice

Letting go of my mistakes   Playing a musical instrument

Success   Driving through the country

Listening to music   Walking on the beach

Empathising   Sewing

Making a decision   Repairing something

Getting praise for a job   Lending a helping hand

Exercise 4

Take a few minutes to read these lists – then put them away and ask yourself:

- What is it that drains my energy?
- What is it that gives me energy and a lift?

Take a few minutes to reflect and create your own table of energy sources and energy drains.

Sources	Drains
• ~~Resting~~	•
•	•
•	•
•	•
•	•

When you have created your list of energy sources and energy drains, notice how many of the sources you are including in your life at this time. Remember, don't judge this, only observe it and accept that for now, it is true.

Optimum stress level

A key concept that permeates the natural world is that of the optimum (the idea that there is a satisfactory level of all things). This is in sharp contrast with the industrial western consciousness that always sees things as maximum or minimum. Too much stress and too little stress can damage our health. People need tension and deadlines and the pressure involved to perform at their best level. Each of us can no doubt remember events which challenged us to give of our best, usually there was an element of tension involved, perhaps in examinations or competitions. These stressing times of tension need to be balanced with times of rest and relaxation. There is an optimum stress level for each person and for the same people under different circumstances. Because this is so, it is very important to develop an awareness of one's own stress proneness and stress points and one's own optimum stress level.

Table F

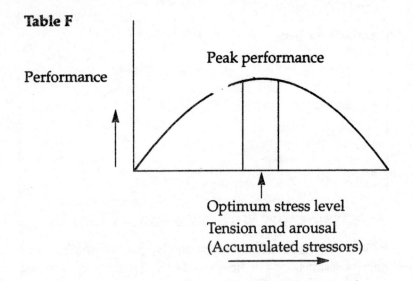

As can be seen from this diagram a person's performance will increase with increased arousal or tension and then will level off and then decrease as stress/arousal increases. It is obvious from this curve that excessive amounts of tension are actually counter-productive. It is not self-indulgent but rather common sense not to allow too many different stressors to accumulate in our lives.

Exercise 5
List ten things that are stressful in your life at this time. Number them in order of seriousness.

Current stressful things	
o	o
o	o
o	o
o	o
o	o
o	o

Examine the list:
   Which of these are positive (p)?
   Which are negative factors (n)?
   Which give you a buzz (b)?
   Which drain your energy (e)?

   Which do you feel:
   (a) in control of (c)?
   (b) not in control of (nc)?

Of those that you do feel in control of: is there anything that you can do to change them or any part of them? Remember, observe all this information: don't judge it.

How do you handle your stressful situations?
Problems and difficulties we encounter in life can be of any nature and at any time. We may deal differently with problems in different areas of our lives and there are a variety of reasons why this is so. One reason for this may be that the type of relationship we have with people varies

and so the issues will evoke different responses. Particular situations or difficulties we encounter may trigger areas of sensitivity for us or put us in contact with issues within ourselves that have not been resolved. Much of the conflict and difficulties we experience in our dealing with others is due in part to unresolved conflicts and issues within ourselves. Problems can be broadly divided into personal, home and work.

The way we respond to problems will, on observation, allow us to discover information about the way we relate to different groups of people. For example, you may cope very differently at work with colleagues than you do at home with a partner or children. This will give you information about yourself, your coping abilities, habits and patterns.

Exercise 6

List a few difficult or stressful situations that you have found yourself in during the past while.

Recent difficult stressful situations
•
•
•
•

Choose
- One that is concerned with home/life issues
- One that is concerned with personal relationship issues
- One that is concerned with work or work-related issues.

Read the following list of thirty possible responses.
   1-12 and 18-30 are for home/life issues/personal
   13-30 are for work-related issues

Table G: Your stress response

Response	Never	Rarely	Periodically	Regularly	Very Often
1 Do some housework/other work	1	2	3	4	5
2 Try to do something where you don't use your mind	1	2	3	4	5
3 Cry on your own	1	2	3	4	5
4 Bottle it up for a time, then break down	1	2	3	4	5
5 Explosive, mostly temper, not tears	1	2	3	4	5
6 Treat yourself to something eg clothes, meals out	1	2	3	4	5
7 Sit and think	1	2	3	4	5
8 Get angry with people or things which cause the problem	1	2	3	4	5
9 Talk things over with lots of friends and express feelings	1	2	3	4	5
10 Go over the problem again and again in your mind to try and understand it	1	2	3	4	5
11 See what insights can be gained	1	2	3	4	5
12 Talk to someone who could do something about the problem	1	2	3	4	5
13 Seek support/advice from supervisors/boss/colleagues	1	2	3	4	5
14 Try to recognise your own limitations	1	2	3	4	5
15 Talk to understanding colleagues and get support	1	2	3	4	5
16 Set priorities and deal with problems accordingly	1	2	3	4	5
17 Accept the situation and learn to live with it	1	2	3	4	5
18 Try not to think about it	5	4	3	2	1
19 Go quiet	5	4	3	2	1
20 Go on as if nothing happened	5	4	3	2	1
21 Keep feelings to yourself — control fears	5	4	3	2	1
22 Avoid being with people	5	4	3	2	1
23 Show a 'brave face'	5	4	3	2	1
24 Worry constantly	5	4	3	2	1
25 Lose sleep	5	4	3	2	1
26 Stop eating	5	4	3	2	1
27 Eat more	5	4	3	2	1
28 Wish that you could change what happened	5	4	3	2	1
29 Have fantasies or wishes about how things might have turned out	5	4	3	2	1
30 Delegate the problem (work issue)	5	4	3	2	1

- Reflect on each of these situations and ask yourself 'In which of the following ways did I respond?'
- Read through all possible responses.

Remember, the purpose of this questionnaire is to assist you to learn about your own coping mechanisms and skills. Don't censor or judge your response. Allow yourself to be open and honest with yourself.

Add up the scores for each situation. Remember, for the work situation only use responses 13-30. For personal or home situations use only responses 1-12 and 18-30.

Results

The score for the personal and home issues should be in the range 25-125. Those for work issues should be in the range 19-95.

20	125
Maladaptive	Adaptive

See how your score fits on this scale for each of your issues. Remember don't judge it. Allow it to show you how you are dealing with certain issues at this moment.

As you reflect on the information you have received about yourself from these exercises and questionnaires you may want to ask yourself: 'What, if anything, can I change?' You may want to ask yourself: 'What, if anything, can I do about all of this?'

If there are several areas of difficulty in our lives, for example, stresses at work coupled with financial stresses and perhaps interpersonal conflicts, dealing with and altering any of these areas creates a change within our whole system. Because this is so, we don't need to dwell on all that we can't change or resolve, but rather begin with the issues where we feel change is possible, however small, and work on resolving these. Once any level of alteration is achieved, we experience a change which gives a sense of hope and relief. Perhaps this is the origin of the expression 'Observe everything, ignore a lot and change a little'.

Change is a normal and natural part of life and is constantly taking place in all areas of life. Yet it is something that we tend to resist and in doing so, often cause ourselves much distress.

Exercise 7

Take a sheet of paper and divide it in two sections.
- In one section list a number of areas in your life where you would **like** things to be different or changed.
- In the second section list **how** you would like each of them to be different. Then divide these into:
* Those that you **can** do something about now or in the near future.
* Those that you **can't** do anything about now or in the near future.

Examine the list of those you can change and ask yourself:
- Am I actually willing to change any of these?
- Which ones can I begin to change today? (For each of these name what your first step will be, no matter how small it is.)
- What would be the consequences of changing these aspects of my life?
- What risks might be involved?
- Could I live with these consequences?

As you do this exercise notice (without judgement) your thoughts and your feelings as you consider the prospect of changing some things in your life.

In the next chapter we will look at some simple yet effective changes that we can make in our lifestyle so that it can be less stressful and so we can experience more joy and success in living

Chapter 3

Stress alleviation

To live is to change and to live wisely is to change often. Change is the only constant there is and yet when we meet it as a component in our lives it seems that our first response is to resist. We find it difficult to freely accept the dynamics of change. Flexibility and the capacity to adapt to new and changing surroundings is the key to survival in the natural world – it always has been so. Those species that survived through the passing of eras and ages were not as popular myth tells us the toughest – but rather those that were sensitive to the changes happening around them and who were able to adapt in response to those changes in ways that ensured their survival. The word 'sensitive' is important and it implies the capacity and necessity for awareness. Awareness also implies a need for sensitivity. So, in fact, we need to develop both an awareness and a sensitivity to ourselves, our lives and the environment around us and to develop the capacity to respond to the changes and demands presented to us.

FIRST STEPS

Many people feel there is little that can be altered in their life. So often people will say: 'But there is nothing that I can change, nothing that I can do about the situation that I'm in.' This has become a conditioned response for many people. Often they believe it to be completely true and are unaware that it is a conditioned response. It may have been true in some circumstances or some situations in the recent or distant past, but it might not be true at this moment. There is no quick fix, no miracle cure for dealing with excessive stress or with the complexities of life at the end of the twentieth century. We are, all of us, products of our belief systems and our conditioning – we are all creatures of habit. Much of our life is lived without too much reflection or focused awareness. Changing our lifestyle and our way of being in the world requires a commitment and takes time. Not that the ideas in themselves or the steps involved are difficult to grasp in theory. The steps are, in fact, very logical and easy at some levels. What stops it being easy to put into practice are certain belief systems that we hold about ourselves, our roles and the way the world is – the way life is, or is meant to be. So, often the first step in challenging a conditioned response is to become aware that it is just that; a conditioned response. Awareness of our conditioning is the first step towards un-learning and letting go of attitudes that have outlived their usefulness.

In the previous chapter we explored some issues connected with lifestyle, stress levels and patterns of response to problems in different areas of life. In this chapter I would like to further explore some areas of life and attitudes that may be stress-provoking and explore simple effective ways that these can be changed.

So, what is your lifestyle? How would you describe it? Would you describe it as enjoyable, challenging, interesting, stressful and occasionally difficult? Or is it difficult, stressful, excessively challenging and not very interesting? Would you describe yourself as happy? Do you feel alive and full of anticipation for the day or do you struggle out of bed with 'Oh no, another day to get through'? The answers to these questions certainly colour the way that we perceive and interact with the world around us and they influence the type of reality we create and experience in the world.

CHANGING LIFESTYLE — WHAT IS POSSIBLE?

When looking at what one can or might change in one's life it is important to examine closely the area or areas of life that cause distress; to isolate, if possible, the actual stressor involved. This type of investigation assures more success and more effective and lasting changes. Fuzziness and lack of clarity about the issues involved are likely to result in us remaining stuck in the distress currently being experienced. This, of course, increases our experience of helplessness and therefore our level of distress.

I would like to list some issues that are often sources of stress, distress and discomfort in the major areas of daily life. This list is not exhaustive. I hope it will stimulate you to construct your own list of the difficulties in different areas of your life.

Work dilemmas
- Too much work or not enough time
- Not enough skills
- Conflict with team
- Lack of clarity about responsibility
- Lack of support from colleagues
- Unrealistic goals and targets
- Not being listened to or taken seriously
- Too little work

Home issues
- Overcrowding
- No personal space
- Conflict between siblings
- Conflict between parents
- Conflict between parents and children
- Lack of time – always rushing
- Lack of order or too much order!
- Too much responsibility
- Feeling unappreciated – I have to do everything, there is no time for me!

Personal or relationship issues
- Lack of confidence of lack of self-esteem
- Not feeling understood
- Feeling alone – lonely
- Conflictional or difficult relationships

- Lack of close friends
- Lack of good health
- Negative thinking
- Not being able to express yourself

As you reflect on this list and your own list you may be prompted to ask some of the following questions:

What can I do to make my home and my work environment less stressful? What, in my thinking about life, can I question and change? Do my relationships with others cause me distress? Perhaps I can look at the way in which I communicate with others and how that is affecting my relationships. Whether your work is within or outside the home, it can be very stressful.

- What, about your work, causes you the most distress?
- What, if anything, can you change?
- What tasks can you delegate?
- How do you use time?
- Do you feel you use your time well or wisely?
- Do you see a need for more organisation in your life?
- What about time management?
- Are you willing to take on questions like these and see if any of the answers might alleviate your levels of distress?
- Are you willing to put in some effort initially to reorganise your thinking and your way of being?
- Do you wish to believe that there is nothing which can be done about anything?

What is important is that when we look at what we can change we must be realistic. There are no miracle cures. If you are a hyperactive type of person, it is unlikely that you can change this in a month or a year. What you can do is focus on small changes – gradual adaptation of your behaviour. Focus especially on the small changes that can have a great significance in your life. For example, if you are very busy at certain periods, you might need to shelve some tasks or take on extra help during that time or delegate some tasks to others. If you find that travelling to and from work is particularly stressful is there anything about that you can alter? Perhaps you can change the time at which you travel. Perhaps you can do breathing exercises at traffic lights instead of fuming. Learn to see red lights as an opportunity to take a small relaxation break. It won't make the lights change any faster – but you will feel better! If you find family shopping a real stress or burden how can you reduce that? Can you go at a time when shops are not so crowded? Can you go without the children? Can you bring your partner and make it an opportunity for time together? Maybe have a little treat together when you have finished. Change a chore into an event!

Time and time-management

Time is plentiful so long as we manage and use it well. Organisation of time and time-management are skills that we often resist but which are well worth the effort invested, since they allow us to maximise the effectiveness of our input while expanding less time and energy. We need to establish a positive relationship with time and see it as an ally instead of an enemy always working against us.

Establishing a good relationship with time requires careful planning, working out schedules and assessing your capabilities. When doing this, it is good to remember that in the world we live in, things often go wrong and most jobs take longer than we first anticipated.

Planning and organising time

We all need to do some planning around how we spend our time and the balance of time spent in various activities. The extent to which this needs to be done in the different areas of our lives depends to a large extent on the type of lifestyle we are involved in and the type of work practice we are engaged in.

If you work in a regular job where other people plan the activities, you may not need to plan schedules of your working year in the same detail as someone who works for themselves. If you work at weekends or at night you may need to plan social activities more carefully than someone who works during weekdays.

However, whether you work within or outside the home, in a company or for yourself, it is very important for you to list goals, tasks and priorities for a given period of time. You may choose a period of one week, one month, three months, six months, or one year, depending on your own needs. Whichever you choose, be realistic when you are planning — remember you need to eat, sleep, relate with others and have some fun. Be sure that you include periods of high pressure and overtime in your planning and be prepared for them.

Remember, just as the map is not the territory but guides you in the territory — so the schedule or plan is not your life and while it can act as a guide, it can also be changed. I know that sometimes I have an inbuilt resistance to being too tied down or too organised (maybe it is something in my spirit). However, I do know that when I am organised it helps me to cut down on stress as long as I don't become overly controlled by the schedule.

One of the important issues with regard to life and schedules is the attitude of flexibility. We must be flexible enough to reschedule, so that we use the schedule as a framework and from that framework we are able to adapt so that the schedule reflects the reality of our circumstances and life in the moment. Life has a habit of surprising us with unexpected and sometimes unwelcome events. Our task, in order to be able to live well, is to respond to the unexpected in addition to the expected and so to enjoy the rich diversity of experiences. It can be very helpful to create a plan for the year in broad outline, showing major events planned, three-monthly and monthly plans with more details, help to focus more closely on events. Weekly plans and daily timetabling are of great help in ensuring that we get the most out of each day. In planning, it is really important to distinguish between priority tasks; between tasks that are essential and those that are non-essential. If priority tasks are listed then those are the ones to focus in on first, each day or week.

Workaholic!

Workaholism, despite popular opinion, does not equal good work or efficiency. We often see the workaholic who works very hard for a certain period of time, takes no break, eats badly and finally gets ill and then is not available for work for a while. The overall result is not only a lack of efficiency and productivity but often damaged health and damaged relationships both at home and in work. So be realistic in your planning and set goals that are attainable. There will be times when work demands are high and the amount of time available at home or for leisure is decreased but if and when this exception becomes the rule then the balance is lost and problems begin to appear.

Leisure

Leisure activities need to be undertaken and to be planned and scheduled. So often after a hard day it is easy to flop in front of the television and watch it aimlessly for several hours – this may do little to counteract the stresses and strains of the day. It is usually much more beneficial after a hard day to consciously do some other activity, such as walking, running, swimming, playing football, golf or tennis. The discipline needed for the activity will take your mind off the stresses completely and the strains and tensions of the day will ease in a way that they will not by watching television passively.

Participation in such activities requires planning and commitment. Human beings are creatures of habit and so respond well to regular patterns. So, doing certain activities at the same time each day or week is very helpful and works well within our body-mind system. Relaxation and leisure time are not luxuries, they are essential to our well-being – even more so because of the high stress level experienced in today's world. When there is a balance between work and play the quality of both and the quality of life and relationships are enhanced. The change in activities between work, leisure and relaxation permits the use of different circuits in the brain – this allows your mind to rest and so you deal more effectively with all life's aspects.

Holidays are important, they allow an opportunity to live differently and to experience different aspects of ourselves, to break out of the routines of the rest of the year. This again uses different circuits in the brain and has a refreshing and re-energising effect on us. When you are planning your week, or day, you need to remember to plan even a little time that you can be alone. We all need company and we also need solitude – we need to stop seeing solitude as a self-indulgent luxury – for healthy living a little solitude is essential. When we spend a lot of time with other people and in crowded places, this needs to be balanced with time alone.

Relationships

Relationships, companionship and friendship are one of the greatest antidotes to many of the stresses we experience in today's world. They need to be nurtured and they need time. If you spend all your time and energy at work, whether in the home or outside it, what will you have left to give to those people with whom you share your life?

Having time to spend with your partner, your children, your parents, your friends and those with whom you live is important. In the busyness of our world today it is easy to get out of the habit of talking and listening to each other, of really knowing what is going on for other people and of being sensitive to them and their needs.

Delegation

In order to create the time we need to live life successfully and with the least amount of distress, sometimes it is necessary to delegate, to allow others become involved in our work and to take part of the load and responsibility. Often we experience in ourselves a great reluctance to delegate – this is just as true for the person who works in the home as for the top-level executive in a large company.

Delegation, in theory, is simple, yet why is it so difficult for people to do?

- What, if any, are your thoughts about delegation?
- What might the consequences be for you if you did delegate some work to others?
- Do you believe that nobody could do the task as well as you?
- Do you like to think of yourself as indispensable?
- What does this say about your perception of yourself and of other people?
- Is doing the task so important to you that you would risk your health and your happiness?

If and when you decide to delegate some tasks to other people, be sure you pick someone who is capable of doing them. Then be willing to spend time training the person so that they understand the tasks and can do them properly. If you don't you may end up with a self-fulfilling prophecy – 'I knew she/he/they couldn't do it'.

When you delegate a job, within reason, allow that person to make some decision about how the job is carried out – this will enhance the other person's skills and confidence and in the long term give you a supportive colleague. So, if you are too busy, why not make a list of tasks you can delegate.

Exercise 1

My attitudes to delegation
• When I think about delegating a job to other people my first reaction is:_____   _____   _____   • Consider for a moment the consequences for you if you could and did delegate some job to someone else.   • How do you feel about that?

If you discover a mental block in yourself to the idea of delegation, then you will need to start to resolve that block before you can proceed with the idea of delegation.

LIFE IS BREATH-TAKING

Life is a balance of breathing in and of letting go of breath! Both are necessary for healthy living. Letting go of the breath is even marginally more important than breathing in. When you don't let go the last breath you can't create the space for the next breath to come in and so your body cannot fill up with new oxygen and new energy.

Try this little experiment:

Exercise 2

- Breathe in as deeply as possible.
- Hold your breath. Don't breathe out!
- Now try to breathe in again!

Only those who dare to let go can be replenished and filled with newness. Every breath we take in fills our body and mind with the oxygen needed by all the cells to carry out the myriad of activities going on all the time. Every out breath is an opportunity to let go of what has been used, of that which is no longer needed by us. With our exhalation we let go of carbon dioxide, of body waste materials, many of which can become toxic to us if not released and in every breath we exhale there is an opportunity to let go of tensions. If we are what we eat, then it is also true that we become as we breathe. How we are breathing at any moment can give us a fairly accurate indication of how we are internally. Our breathing is often considered to be a mirror of our psyche.

Learning to breathe

Breathing is one of life's autonomic processes, that is, it happens automatically without our having to think: 'Now I must breathe'. The good news is that we can voluntarily change the way that we breathe. This is very important since the way we breathe influences the functions of the autonomic nervous system and whether our response to an event will be the 'fight or flight' or 'relaxation' response (see Chapter 1). Upper-chest breathing stimulates the part of the autonomic nervous system which triggers the fight or flight response, while abdominal breathing stimulates the part of the autonomic nervous system that triggers the relaxation response.

Postures and breathing

As babies, we all know how to breathe properly and naturally. As we grow up we are conditioned into many habits and practices that are quite unnatural but which are considered normal. Much of what is needed as adults is to unlearn the bad habits and bad postures that we come to accept as normal. What does natural, normal breathing look like? Looking at a baby or an animal like a dog or a cat while they breathe, gives a glimpse of what natural breathing is. As we have been schooled into postures which insist on tummies being held in tightly, chests out and buttocks tightly held, it is indeed no wonder that we breathe incorrectly! The posture which adults assume as natural and normal actually serves to cut us off from the centre of power in the body – often referred to as the Hara in the Japanese medical system. It may come as a surprise to us westerners to learn that the centre of the body is in the belly and not in the head!

Other postures, such as a slouching, cause the rib-cage and the chest to be slumped – this results in the breath being confined to the upper chest area, putting much unnecessary stress on our bodies, especially on our lungs and heart.

The effect of breathing on our health and well-being is also affected by the quality of air we breathe. Where possible do breathing exercises near an open window or in open air. Ensure an adequate supply of fresh air in your work or home place. Make sure you get out in the country air or a park at least sometimes!

Abdominal breathing always occurs when we are truly relaxed. What we need to develop is an awareness about how we are breathing at any moment. We need to develop the capacity to switch into abdominal breathing and the relaxation mode, at will. This capacity then gives us great tools and skills to deal with the stresses experienced in the traffic jam, the long queues in public places, and the difficult interactions during any day.

Exercise 3

Relaxing and clearing the mind using the breath

- Remember an incident where you were frightened or angry.
- As you focus on this incident can you recall how you were breathing?
- Now remember a moment of deep happiness or joy.
- As you focus on this moment recall how you were breathing.
  Be aware of the difference.

- Now focus your attention on some present or future event about which you are worried.
- Allow your mind to get caught up in thinking about this problem.
- Notice your breathing.
- Stop and pay attention to each breath as it comes into your body and as it leaves your body.
- Do this for sixty seconds, bringing your attention back each time it wanders.

Now how is your mind?

When we focus attention on the breath it allows the mind to relax and become calm. Therefore, to focus attention on your breathing is a very simple and effective way to clear your mind and allows you to think more clearly and act more effectively.

Exercise 4

How am I breathing?

If you wish to find out how you are breathing at any time, stand or sit and place one hand on your upper chest and one hand on your navel. Don't change your breathing, simply observe your breath and your body's response as you take in and exhale five breaths.

- If only your chest moves then you are using upper chest breathing.
- If your belly expands as you breath in then you are using more of your lungs.

If you find yourself breathing into your upper chest only then you need to change this.

Exercise 5

Changing from upper chest to abdominal breathing

- Breathe in a deep breath and exhale completely through your mouth while making the sound 'choo'. This should evacuate all the air in the lungs and create a vacuum which will draw the next breath into the lower regions of the lungs.
- Allow the next breath to come into your body of its own accord. Notice if your belly expands with this breath. If it doesn't then you need to repeat the complete exhalation.
- Continue now to breathe deeply into the abdomen and exhale fully. Feel the abdomen rise and fall with the breath.

Exercise 6

Abdominal breathing: calming the mind

Any time you are stressed or anxious you can choose to relieve the situation by breathing deeply into the abdomen and fully releasing the breath.
- It may help to see your body filling up with breath like a balloon fills with air as you inhale and feel the balloon emptying as you exhale.
- Exhale fully before you take in the next breath.
- Continue this deep, quiet breathing for three to five minutes. This will calm your mind, relax your body and restore your energy.

Exercise 7

This exercise exaggerates the exhalation and is an excellent way to discharge or release frustration, anger or any strong feelings. It also helps to clear the mind. It can be done seated or standing.

Releasing frustration

- Raise both arms above your head.
- Breathe in through your mouth, then quickly breathe out through your mouth making the sound 'choo'.
- As you breathe out bring down your arms and head as if you were chopping wood.
- Breathe in again slowly and repeat the exercise.

This exercise should only be done twice.

Exercise 8

Centering is a term used to describe the process of gathering resources within yourself. So, before you begin an exam, an interview or a demanding task, take a few moments to complete the following exercise.

X

Centering before an important task
• Place your hands on your navel. • Breathe slowly and deeply. • Exhale deeply, feeling the rise and fall of your abdomen as you do. • As you breathe in gather yourself, your thoughts and your resources into yourself. • As you breathe out release any anxieties, negative thoughts or worries about the task in hand. • Continue this process for a few minutes. • When you are finished you will return to your next activity calm and alert.

Breathing problems

Hyperventilation is caused by faulty breathing and it causes unpleasant physical and mental conditions. Some of the symptoms associated with hyperventilation are dizziness, fainting, sweating, numbness, chest pains and palpitations – these occur owing to excessive loss of carbon dioxide in the body and due to a disturbance of the oxygen/carbon dioxide balance.

Many stress-related illnesses including panic or anxiety attacks are associated with hyperventilation. There is often a vicious cycle set up where, when one experiences anxiety the breathing worsens and the symptoms increase in intensity.

Learning to breathe properly can help to alleviate the problems of hyperventilation. Proper breathing can in fact help to overcome anxiety attacks and help you get back in control. So if you suffer from anxiety attacks – when the next one strikes you stop for a moment and begin to focus your attention on your breath. Continue to breathe as deeply as possible and to focus your attention on the breath and feel the anxiety lessen.

Many breathing exercises are based on yoga principals and many of them are designed for long relaxation sessions. However as an immediate and constantly available resource your breath is an invaluable stress management tool. You always have it with you. It doesn't cost anything. For stress-free living remember, life is breath-taking and letting it flow!

Chapter 4

Learning to relax

Letting go, believe it or not is a key to healthy, happy successful living. Knowing when to let go and when to hold on is a central tenet of successful living. Knowing what things are worth fighting for and what are not— what to struggle for and what not to, allows us to conserve our energy for useful issues. Relaxation is not something we do but something that happens when we let go of tension.

'If you let go a little you have a little peace.

If you let go a lot you have a lot of peace'.

Achaan Chah— Chinese Sage.

Being in a relaxed state of mind is not a passive, limp or ineffective state but one which is a dynamic, ever adapting balance of arousal and relaxation finely tuned to meet the demands of the moment. We sometimes believe that if we are tense then we will be able to work and think better. This of course is not true.

- Try tensing up your body and your face really tight – now try to make a list of tasks that need doing – how was that?
- Now stand up, shake out the tension and take two or three breaths - now make the list.
- Which was easier and more efficient?

Too much tension prevents you achieving your deepest potential.

Negative thoughts

Negative thoughts or emotional states make it difficult to operate from a clear mind space.

- Remember an issue that evoked anger in you.
- Now that you have contacted that emotion, try to repress it — shove it down in yourself.
- Now try to concentrate on an issue, or have a conversation with somebody.

I'm sure that you found that difficult.

Relaxation is something that we may have done naturally as a small baby but, like many other natural skills, it gets lost in our growing up and we need, as adults, to relearn these skills. Relearning as adults can be difficult because we have to let go of so much of our conditioning — much of which has, by now, an appearance of normality about it. The way we do lots of adult things may seem normal, but there is little natural about them.

Learning relaxation skills and using them in our daily life can enhance the way we deal with the distress and tension of life. These tensions can then be seen as opportunities to apply skills and to refine them and develop them further.

KEYS TO LEARNING RELAXATION SKILLS

- **Self awareness**: constantly developing an awareness of who you are this moment. Develop care and consideration for yourself and who you are at this moment. Appreciate that the life process is in fact the great teacher and by being open we can grow from life's unending challenges.
- **Commitment** and **courage**: these are necessary to help change from a belief that you need excessive stress. This stress robs you of your best potential.
- **Developing relaxation skills**: this will increase your capacity for concentration in all areas of your life. It is also a sound foundation for any practise of meditation. When you know how to relax you don't need to feel traumatised by the experience of being stressed. Each time you let go you prepare yourself to meet your next stressor graciously.
- **Define your motives**: before you think about learning

to relax ask yourself 'Is this another should?' Am I doing it because I feel I should do it, to please others, or am I choosing to do this because it is something that I believe can help me to live life more fully and be more at peace?' The more at peace you are within yourself the more at peace you are in the world and the more peaceful the world is. If you find yourself doing it from the place of should, ask yourself how that might change. What do you need to do to change this?

LEARNING TO RELAX: WHAT YOU NEED

Motivation

What is important when learning any skill is patience. When each of us learned to walk or to ride a bicycle we fell and stumbled lots of times. Yet we continued because we wanted to learn and it excited us. You can't learn to relax when you are under severe pressure or acute deadlines, just as you can't learn to swim when you have fallen overboard from a boat. So if you want to be able to use skills of relaxation during times of distress, then you must learn them during periods of quietness.

Regular practice

At first you need to set aside ten or twenty minutes, once or twice per day to learn the skills. You can also practice many of the skills at other times during the day.

Choose a schedule that is possible for you to have one twenty-minute or two ten-minute time periods.

If you are a person who is constantly busy or hurrying you may find this difficult. Be sure you don't set it up in such a way as to create failure for yourself. If this does happen, instead of judging yourself as a failure allow it to be an opportunity when you can examine the 'how come' of it: 'How come it is so difficult for me to commit myself to this? What, if anything, does this tell me about myself, my belief system or the ideas that govern my life?' Remember, criticism interferes with learning and growth.

Don't judge, just accept and observe. Everything we experience in life can help our growth. So be open to the experience!

Quiet environment

This means you need a place where no noise, no telephones, no interfering sounds can interrupt you.

Focus your mind

To focus the mind, use your breath (see centering exercise, p. 60), gaze at a candle or use a mantra (a repeated phrase) to help you.

Balance

Balance is needed between control and wandering of the mind. The analogy that is often used is holding a bird in your hand. If you hold it too tight you will kill it, too loosely it will fly away. Don't try to make anything happen. Remember relaxation is what happens when you let go of tension.

General rules for any relaxation:

• Allow relaxation to happen.
• Don't make huge efforts to relax.
• Adopt an attitude of 'nowhere to go and nothing to do'.
• Just allow yourself to be.

Each time you exhale a breath let go into gravity and exhale the tension or stresses you experience in your body or mind.

Posture

A straight spine allows the flow of energy. Lying down can cause drowsiness or sleepiness; so do your relaxation exercises in a comfortable sitting position if this happens to you .

Use a tape

When learning relaxation at first you might want to use a tape with instructions to guide you through the relaxation steps.

Timing

Timing is vital, so choose a time when you are not too tired or exhausted or too hungry or full or too hyped up.

Distraction

Distraction is the great obstacle that most of us have to overcome in learning relaxation skills. There are two types of distractions: external ones such as noise, cold or heat, can be overcome much more easily than internal distractions, such as thoughts, wandering, physical sensations, pain, discomfort or boredom.

One way to deal with these is to acknowledge that they are present but not to focus too much attention on them, neither try to deny or repress them.

Each time you wander, gently bring your mind back without judgement to an awareness of your breath and this present moment.

Remember you, not your mind, is in control, so each time your mind wanders take control and bring it back gently and without judgement. Above all, be patient with yourself. One of the key components in relaxation is breathing and breath control.

COMPLETE BODY RELAXATION

Exercise 1

Try this exercise for an experience of complete relaxation:

- Find a place which is quiet and where you are unlikely to be disturbed.
- Make sure the temperature is suitable; not too hot or too cold. Wear loose clothing or loosen any belts.
- You can do the relaxation lying on the floor or sitting upright on a straight chair. Make sure your spine is straight as this helps the energy to flow.
- You may wish to speak the instructions onto a tape and use it or use one of the commercially available relaxation tapes to guide you.

- You may wish to use quiet music (flute solos are very suitable) to help create a quiet atmosphere.
- You may wish to light a candle.
- Begin by focusing your mind – you can do this by paying attention to your breath. As you breathe in, be aware of breathing in; as you breathe out, be aware of breathing out.
  Repeat a phrase like 'peace', 'calm', 'serenity'. Relax each time you breathe out. This helps to calm and quieten your mind and frees you from agitation.
- As you settle into the quietness, assure yourself that you will relax deeply during this time and that it will refresh and energise you for the rest of your day or evening.
- Begin by bringing your awareness into your feet.
  Be aware of your toes, wiggle them.
  Rotate your ankles.
  Allow yourself to become aware of any tension in your feet and as you breathe out, release the tension and feel your feet becoming heavy.
- Now move your attention to your legs.
  Be aware of your calves, your knees, shins, thighs, hips.
  Be aware of any tension that is present there.
  As you exhale, imagine the tension leaving with the breath. Feel your legs relax and sink into the chair or the floor.
- Now your attention is focused on your genitals and your pelvic area.
  Notice any holding of tension and as you breathe out, feel the tension being released.
- Bring your attention to the abdominal area and notice any tightness or pain. As you breathe out, release the tension and feel your breath deepening.
- Bring your awareness now to your lower back. Notice any holding of tension as you breathe in, feel the breath relaxing any tension in your back. Feel it dissolve as you exhale.
- Now focus your attention in the mid and upper back region. Feel the tension dissolving as you exhale. Move your attention now to your chest. As you breathe

deeply and smoothly feel the tension in the chest area dissolving and flowing out with the exhalation.

- Bring your attention now to your shoulders.
  Be aware of any tightness or holding and as you breathe out, feel your shoulders drop.
- Now bring your awareness to your throat, neck, head and face. Be aware of any tightness or tension in facial or other muscles. Allow the muscles to relax. Allow your jaw to drop, feel yourself smile.
- Now bring your attention to your arms and hands.
  Be aware of any holding tension. As you breathe out, feel it all drain away with your breath.
- Now pause for a moment.
  Scan your body.
  Is there some place still holding tension? If so, bring your attention to that place. Feel the tension melting even slightly as you focus your attention there. Then, as you breathe out, allow the tension to flow, leaving you more relaxed.
- Now allow yourself to rest in this quiet space for five or ten minutes. Focus your mind completely on your breath coming and going or on a phrase like: 'I'm calm and centered', 'I am at peace', or one that is appropriate for you.

When you are ready say to yourself: 'I'm alert and calm and refreshed', slowly move your body and bring your awareness back to your present surroundings, open your eyes and stretch.

Exercise 2

Sometimes it is difficult to relax on demand. We try to relax and nothing happens. Often this can be helped by the following type of relaxation exercise, which involves a tensing of the muscles followed by a relaxation. This is done with different groups of muscles throughout the body. It also allows one to experience, in a very real way, the difference between tensed and relaxed muscles.

- Begin by lying on the floor or sitting upright in a chair. Close your eyes but don't squeeze them tightly.

- Start with your feet: make a fist with your toes and tense your feet as hard as feels comfortable. Hold this for a few seconds and then exhale and let the tension go. Stretch out the feet, feel the tingle of relaxation.
- Now inhale and tense your legs and thighs as hard as feels comfortable. Hold for a few seconds and release the tension as you exhale.
- Inhale as you tense your buttocks – hold the tension for a few seconds then release and let go as you exhale.
- Inhale again and as you do tense your stomach by pushing it out – hold this tension for a few seconds then exhale and relax.
- Now move to the chest, as you inhale feel your chest expand – hold this expanded position for a few moments and then relax it when you exhale.
- As you inhale tense your back, especially in between your shoulder blades. Hold the tension for a few seconds and then release it as you exhale.
- Now tense the whole trunk of the body – and experience the tension – breathe out, let the tension go – relax.
- Now tense your shoulders by lifting them up towards your ears as you breathe in – hold for a few seconds and relax, dropping the shoulders as you breathe out.
- Clench your fists as tightly as possible and feel the tension in your hands and arms. Hold the tension. Now let it go and shake out the arms and hands.
- Move your attention to your head and face. Scrunch up your face, tightening all the face muscles – hold the tension – now release it and relax and let go as you exhale. Inhale and yawn with open mouth and raised eyebrows. Hold for a second then release and let go.
- Remain lying or sitting and focus your attention on your breathing – allow your breath to be slow and deep and even.

Stay focused on your breath for five or ten minutes and each time you exhale feel it release more of the tension. It might be helpful to say 'calm', 'relax', 'peace' or another suitable word, to yourself, as you exhale.

Visualisation to bring calmness, peace, serenity

A visualisation is just that: something for you to imagine or visualise. This visualisation can be done at any time during the day. It might be most effective in the morning as you start the day or in the evening before bed. Make sure you choose a time and place where you will not be disturbed during the 15-20 minutes required to do this.

Exercise 3

- Choose a room or space that is comfortable, not too hot or too cold. You might wish to speak the instructions into a tape and use this to guide you.
- Begin by finding a position in which your body is comfortable. You may sit or lie. Become aware of your breath, without needing to change or control it. Just be aware of your breath as it comes into your body and as it leaves your body. Note the rise and fall of your breath, the ebb and flow of the breath coming and going into your body.
- As you exhale say 'relax', 'serene', 'calm' or any other words that are appropriate for you. Allow your attention to move to different parts of your body. If you find a place in your body that is holding tension then focus your attention on that place. Imagine that as you inhale the breath is going to that tense place in your body, feel the breath gently massage the area and as you exhale, feel the breath carry with it the tension, leaving your body relaxed and clam.
- For the next five breaths exhale as deeply as is comfortable and with each exhalation allow yourself to sink deeper into the centre of your own being. As you find this calm, deep place within yourself, I invite you, in your imagination, to find yourself at a beach on a beautiful warm sunny day strolling along the water's edge where you come to a boat.
- Step into the boat, and set out towards an island that is

143

Page 33
,, 45
,. 50
,, 60

visible and not too far from the shore. You feel so safe and cared-for as you gently cross the water in your boat. As you journey further away from the shore you feel a wonderful sense of calmness and freedom. Away from all the cares of your everyday life – the sunshine creates jewels in the ocean and you feel drenched with sunlight and healing.

- Finally you arrive on the island and step out of your boat, onto the sand, which is white and warm.
- You walk along this beautiful beach aware of the wonders of this place – the birds singing, the music of the sea as waves lap on the shore, the warmth of the sun on your body.
- You lie down and almost merge with the sand as you become aware of your own place in the universe and of your connection with all that is.
- You rest in this deep knowing and as you do, you feel yourself and your energy being replenished and you are filled with vitality and joy.
- Now you rest here for as long as is comfortable for you. (You might want to put on relaxing music on your instructions tape at this point for whatever length of time you wish to rest, 5-10 minutes.)
- When you are fully refreshed – you become aware again of a voice calling you back. You begin your return journey by walking back to the boat and returning over the sea to the beach from where you began the journey. Back on the beach again you become aware of your body and your breathing – gently aware of your body and your breathing – gently opening your eyes and stretching. As you return to your usual waking consciousness say to yourself: 'I am refreshed and revitalised. I carry this new energy with me as I move in the next activity, whatever that may be'.

MUSCLE STRETCHES AND RELAXATION

We hold tension in all parts of our bodies, in groups of muscles we are familiar with and in ones we hardly know we own. All muscles can exist in a tense or relaxed mode

71

and when they hold tension for too long without being relaxed they contract and get shorter and tighter and we experience this as body stress. Stress is cumulative and so if we don't release the tension and stress from our bodies it just builds up.

The back, chest, shoulder, neck and face are major areas of tension-holding in the body. These areas tend to accumulate tension during the day depending on the activities we are engaged in. Stretching is an excellent way to offset the tension picked up by muscles.

Here are some very simple and easy exercises that can relieve the build-up of tension in the body in these groups of muscles.

Exercise 4

Neck, head and face relaxation: exercises to relax the head neck and face can be done easily anytime and in most places during your working day.

Head rolls: head rolls ease out the tension and will be most beneficial if done slowly.
- Drop your chin onto your chest as you breathe out.
- Now rotate your head slowly clockwise as you inhale.
- When your head is back in an upright position exhale and continue to exhale as you rotate your head until your chin is again on your chest.
- Do this three times and then repeat three times in the opposite direction.

Head and neck stretches: stretching and turning your head and neck slowly helps to relieve neck tension.
- Slowly move your head from side to side while keeping it level.
- Gently move your head forward and back as far as is comfortably possible.
- Move it to the left and the right. Feel the stretch on the muscles.

This exercise is good for relieving stress from driving or sitting at a desk writing or typing.

Exercise 5

Stretches for shoulders: to relax the shoulders and upper back try the following in a sitting position.

- Place your right hand on your right shoulder and your left hand on your left shoulder.
- Bring your elbows together in front of your chest and make slow large circles first in one direction and then in the opposite direction, as if you are painting a large circle with your elbow.
- Feel the ease in your shoulders.

or try this one:
- Lift your shoulder up to your ears and squeeze.
- Feel the tension.
- Now drop your shoulders and relax.
- Feel the relief.

or try this one:
- Stand and stretch (this can also be adapted to seated or lying).
- Check that you are comfortable before you start – spine tall, neck free – breathing naturally.
- Raise your hands slowly above your head.
- Link your fingers and slowly turn your palms out to face the sky.
- Breathe in and stretch your palms higher, straightening your arms.
- Feel the lengthening of your spine and the stretch in your shoulders.
- Feel the stretch then pause.
- Breathe out and return your hands to the side of your body.
- Repeat as often as is comfortable.

Exercise 6

Stretches for the middle and upper back: this can be done while standing but can be adapted to seated or lying position.

- Stand tall and feel comfortable – breathe normally.

- Slowly raise your arms sideways until they are stretched above the head with fingers long.
- Hands should not touch.
- Slowly and gently bend slightly to the right and slowly come back to the centre and gently bend to the left and back to the centre again. The top of your body is like the branches of a tree. Listen to your body and move in a way which is comfortable for you.
- Lower the arms and rest.
- Feel the difference in your waist and upper back.
- Try to keep this a side bend and not lean forwards or back — rather like moving between two panes of glass.

Or try this one:
- Stand with your feet wider than your shoulders.
- Feel the strength in your legs and spine.
- Stand tall with your body relaxed.
- Slowly raise your arms sideways until they are at shoulder level.
- Breathe normally.
- Turn the palms of your hands out to face the wall.
- As you breathe in press your palms further out towards the wall.
- Now let the breath out slowly as you lower your arms slowly to the sides of your body.
- Feel the lovely stretch across the back.
- This opens up the chest and allows fuller breathing.
- This exercise can be done seated only.

Exercise 7

Tense tummy relaxation

- Lie on your back and hold your knees gently.
- Breathe in deeply.
- When breathing out draw the knees tightly together towards the chest with the hands.

It is important that you don't push yourself too far with any of these exercises. There is really no relaxational benefit in the 'make it burn' attitude. With each exercise as you breathe out allow your body to stretch into the exercise to the extent that is comfortable for your body.

Exercise 8
General relaxation: this exercise is one that I find very helpful in the release of tension during a busy day or after a long drive.

- Put your feet and legs onto a chair and rest your back and head on the floor (or put your legs and feet against the wall and your back and head on the floor).
- Place your hands one on your navel and one on your chest.
- Focus your attention on your breath for a few minutes keeping your eyes softly closed.
- If your eyes are tired rub your hands together and place the palms of your hands in front of your eyes.
- Open your eyes and allow them to rest in the darkness of your palms.
- This inverted position is not suitable for any person who has high blood pressure – so if you suspect you have high blood pressure don't do this exercise as outlined above. You could sit on a chair with your feet on a stool, cover your eyes with the palms of your hands and focus on your breath for a few minutes.

(My thanks to Liz Comerton, Belfast yoga teacher and stress management consultant, for permission to reproduce these exercises.)

STRESS-PROOFING BY DIET

There are certain foods that make us feel full of energy and others that pull our energy level down. There are foods whose interactions with our body chemistry increases nervousness, irritability and, hyperactivity and when we eat these foods we experience those states in ourselves. Much attention has been focused on the effects of additives in foods consumed mostly by children where there has been wide-scale connection between certain additives and hyperactive behaviour.

Because food can give or drain energy, it is important that we become more aware of what we are eating and how it may affect us. One of the characteristics of food and food production is that it is not as natural as it was in previous times. Many of the processes involved in producing bright colourful fruit and vegetables all year round may in fact reduce the nutritional content or they may have additives in them, which are not health promoting. The vast array of processed and refined food products while providing convenient and easy to prepare meals may contain chemicals that are really quite damaging to health. Good food and good nutrition is a very important aspect of healthy living. It is an area that we can make choices about especially as our basic knowledge of nutrition increases. It is an area of life over which each of us can exercise a large degree of control.

Adopting a healthy diet

The key to healthy nutrition is balance (as with so much else in the natural world). Over the past number of years there have been many claims and counter-claims about the health benefits or damage to health of certain foods. Some of those have resulted in healthier diets and lifestyles.

- A healthy diet needs to contain protein, carbohydrate, fat, vitamins, minerals and fibre.
- It needs to contain a minimum amount of chemical additives.
- A diet which is healthy and balanced will contain a mixture of raw and cooked foods.
- It will contain fruits, vegetables, meat, fish, grains, nuts, pulses and fibre.
- The fresher the food the more nutrients present in it.
- Organically-grown fruit and vegetables are healthier since they contain no pesticides.
- When preparing non-organic vegetables — soak for few minutes in water to which a tablespoon of vinegar has been added — this helps remove pesticides from vegetables.
- Organically-produced free range eggs, poultry and

meat are also a better choice since they contain no
growth promoting hormones or antibiotics.

- Using whole grains provides essential fibre in diet, as
do fruit and vegetables.
- White flour and white rice have much of the fibrous
outer layers removed and so are less beneficial in the
diet.
- At different times we may need supplements of
vitamins or minerals. Usually the quantity needed is
small – however the absence of these in the body can
cause us to feel tired and lacking in energy.

The question of diet in a health-promoting lifestyle needs
to be approached sensibly. It is important not to allow
food to become yet another source of worry or stress in
our lives. What is important is that our diet contains a
balance of major food groups with small amounts of
animal fats, and that our food is cooked in a way that
preserves the nutritional content – so don't boil away all
the goodness in the vegetables and then throw it out with
the water! It is important to eat food slowly and to enjoy it.
Presentation is also important – I find that even when I eat
alone I like to set the table nicely and sit down and enjoy
the food. Blessing the food and giving thanks for it in
whatever way might be appropriate for you may also
enhance the experience of eating and being nourished by
the food.

A common dilemma is that at the time when we most
need not to add yet another stressor to our load we do so
by the food we eat! When you are running around in
overdrive gear how often do you find yourself eating
snacks instead of a meal? At these times how often do you
eat standing up or, worse still, rushing out the door? And
what kind of snacks do you indulge in?

Under stressful conditions we often increase our
consumption of foods such as coffee, tea, alcohol, sugary
foods, spicy foods, and food with high fat content.

Looking at the diagram which follows, it is obvious that
eating like this is a sure way to increase your stress level
and yet it is exactly what we do much of the time!

Table H: Relationship between food and stress

Food	Physical effects	Consequences	Healthy alternatives
High sugar content Biscuits, jams, cakes, chocolates, sweets, drinks, honeys, relishes, desserts, processed foods containing hidden sugar	Floods bloodstream giving instant energy high for short time and temporarily relieving physical tiredness	Adrenal glands overworked, less effective regulation of blood stream. Increased tiredness. Increased depression. Increased irritability	Sugar-free jam, apple butter, apple and pear spread, blackstrap molasses, muesli, carob chocolate substitute, raisins, dates, figs, dried fruit, fresh fruit juices
High saturated fat content Fatty red meat, pork, bacon, sausages, hamburgers, lard, suet, dripping, hard margarine, full-fat milk, cream, full-fat yoghurt, fried foods, butter, full-fat cheese, hidden fats in sauces, dressings, soups	Leads to an increase in production of cholesterol in the liver	Increases the level of cholesterol in the blood stream. This can lead to a clogging of arteries	Lean chicken, fish, game, polyunsaturated vegetable oils and margarines, skimmed milk, low-fat yoghurt, cottage cheese, goat's milk cheese
High salt content Crisps, chips, salted nuts, processed foods that use salt as a preservative	Works with potassium to regulate the body's fluid balance	High blood pressure. Stimulates adrenal glands, stimulating stress arousal	Decrease salt in cooking. Eat raw unsalted nuts, pumpkin seeds, sunflower seeds, raw vegetables, seaweed

Food	Physical effects	Consequences	Healthy alternatives
Caffeine Coffee, tea, cola drinks, some pain-killers	Mimics stress arousal: directs stimulus of nervous system, increased alertness; stimulates heart, kidneys, adrenal glands; dilates blood vessels	Irritates kidneys; headaches, lethargy, irritability, muscular fatigue, nervousness, palpitations	Herbal teas, decaffeinated coffee, dandelion coffee, fresh vegetable and fruit juices, spring water
Alcohol Wine, beer, spirits, cider	Dilates blood vessels, raises blood sugar levels, relaxes body and mind, stimulates appetite and digestion	When taken in excess: liver damage, blood sugar problems, impaired judgement and brain function, poor co-ordination, depression, dependence on alcohol	Low alcohol beer/wine, dealcoholised wine, water

Changing patterns

At times of high stress levels we tend to eat more hamburgers, chips and cheese, all of which can increase our cholesterol level. This is very serious because under stressful conditions the body manufactures its own cholesterol – thus we need to decrease the intake of high cholesterol foods during periods of high stress arousal. High salt intakes increase nervous tension, fluid retention and blood pressure, so high salt foods such as peanuts, crisps and chips are certainly not what our bodies need during stressful times.

As you look at the table of stress promoting foods, try not to respond by thinking 'I have to change everything I eat'. Ask yourself rather, 'What small changes can I introduce into my eating patterns that might reduce the stress component caused by food?'

Useful susggestions
- Grill instead of fry
- Use baked potatoes instead of chips
- Cut down your coffee consumption gradually by one cup per day
- Cut down slightly the amount of salt in cooking
- Add more fruit and raw or almost raw vegetables to your diet
- Change from white bread to brown bread, white rice to brown rice - in some of the meals you cook
- Drink lots of water - it is a key component in a healthy eating plan.

Since you have a large role to play in the food you eat, it is important to use the elements of awareness, choice and responsibility in this area as in any other area of your life. If you become aware that eating certain foods evokes a particular physical and emotional reaction in you then you may need to ask yourself 'Do you wish to continue to eat this food and am I willing to live with the consequences?' If you choose to eat the food do so freely and don't add the extra stress of feeling guilty about eating the 'wrong' food!

If you have been eating foods with high sugar, salt, fat or alcohol content for some time, it helps to take a break from this diet and allow your body to recover from the stress associated with these foods. A few days of simple eating – mainly vegetables and rice – and drinking plenty of water will help rebalance your system. A fruit or fruit juice day can restore your energy greatly. If you do this, be careful not to bring in the often familiar judgmental attitude and sense of punishing yourself. If you choose to fast or abstain from certain foods do so but not to punish yourself, rather to rebalance your body and clear your mind. Fasting can be a joyful experience and when the body has only a little food to process it can regenerate. Fasting for more than a day or so needs to be carefully planned and if you are in any doubt about your capacity to fast – check it with a doctor. You also need to choose a time when you are not busy with other projects, otherwise it may add to your stress load.

Prevention is always more desirable than cure. In looking at what we can do to reduce and combat the stress in our lives we need to consider several different aspects of the situation. We need to ascertain what are our needs during a particular period of our lives. What daily and weekly and monthly stress-proofing strategies can we employ that will deal with the stress and strains we are experiencing.

ANTIDOTES TO STRESS

Earlier in this book we considered the areas of relaxation, breathing, muscle stretching and diet as ways of alleviating stress. Regular exercise is also a great antidote to stress. What is important when choosing an exercise is to pick one that you enjoy

Exercise

- Brisk walking is one of the most effective and beneficial forms of exercise. It is free and can be done almost anywhere. It requires no equipment other than supportive shoes.
- Swimming is also an excellent exercise. Both walking and swimming are aerobic exercises, which means that they work by increasing the body's oxygen consumption, raising the heart rate and making the lungs and arteries expand.
- Football, tennis and golf also provide good forms of exercise. Again in the area of exercise, moderation is important – be gentle with your body. Listen to your body and allow it to tell you its limits rather than you imposing limits from a place of 'I should be able to'.

81

- Find a regular time each day or each week to exercise – be sure to pick a suitable time – so that you don't sabotage your plans.

Importance of sleep

Sleep is also a valuable ally in our battle with excess stress. It is important to get enough sleep each night or on balance over a week. I don't believe that all people need the same amount of sleep – or that the same people necessarily need the same amount of sleep all the time. Sometimes people actually worry about their lack of sleep because they didn't sleep a certain number of hours. The quality of your sleep is as important as the quantity. What is important is that when you go to sleep you are relaxed and free from worries. One of the things I believe is unhelpful is to watch violent films or even news programmes just before sleep because we may bring much of these disturbed images into our sleep.

Humour and pleasure

Another very important component in a healthy life is humour. Learning to laugh at yourself and life is a great tonic and it is something we all need in our lives. So be sure that you can have some fun in your life each day or each week!

Another way that can help to unstress you or help you to deal effectively with stress is to pamper yourself! I can almost hear you say 'self indulgent': yes it is and it is okay! Pampering yourself, within your budget of money, time and resources, is a wonderful antidote to stress and strain! If you have difficulties with the word or the idea of pampering yourself, check out where that is coming from! How can you pamper yourself? Each person has their own ideas about what a really pampering experience is for them:

- An ice-cream cone
- A slice of cake
- A massage

- Having a long soak in the bath with aromatherapy oils
- Staying in bed until dinner-time with a good book
- Having breakfast in bed
- Going out for a meal
- Buying yourself a treat
- Buying flowers
- Employing someone to do housework occasionally

You no doubt have lots of other ideas. When you decide on the way you will pamper yourself – get into the ideal frame of mind that this is a special treat for you – enjoy it fully – celebrate yourself and your capacity to pamper yourself! Be indulgent – you deserve it. Remember pampering yourself within your budget is an act of self-care, self-love and you don't need to apologise for it!

Planning

Most people have periods in their lives when they are more stressed and busier than normal, times when the pressure of events is severe. During such times, it is important to take extra care not to allow the stress levels to escalate. One of the difficulties is that often when we are under severe stress we don't actually know what we need, nor are we able to give ourselves that which we need when we discover it. However, practising the relaxation and breathing exercises during such times will help to deal with these periods of excess stress. When the stressful time is over we need to rest – take time out, allow adequate time to unwind and to allow the body and mind to find its new balance-point. This requires careful planning, especially if you work for yourself.

Daily routines of relaxation, exercises, breathing and good nutrition are a major contribution to stress-proofing yourself during the normal times in the year when life is progressing at its ordinary pace.

The result of practices like this is to change your internal environment and your attitude. This gives you more options and more skills to deal with the external world, no matter what it presents to you.

Using relaxing/breathing skills during stress-filled moments in the day ensures that stress does not build up in you and in fact allows you an opportunity to relax and regenerate your energy.

Sometimes we need to concede that we can't change the external environment but we can change our attitude to it and when that happens everything changes. One of the important issues to remember is: 'I can change me but I can't change you'.

As we review these and other suggestions for stress-proofing, in our present world, each person needs to ask themselves: 'What is it that I need to do in my life to decrease the stress levels, to increase happiness and joy in the way I live?'

CHANGES FOR LIFE

Exercise 9
Examine the checklist of changes that you might like to make in your life by completing the following:

Home-life and personal relationship
• Develop good and open relationships with those who are close to you. Take time to allow this to happen. • Take time to be alone. • Deal with, rather than avoid, conflictional issues. • Find an exercise routine that suits you. • Eat a healthy balanced diet. • Celebrate often. Create little celebrations. Make family occasions out of meal times. • Laugh often. • Breath out.

Work
• Plan your work load carefully – choose priorities, make lists. • Delegate work if possible. • Change your travelling time if it is stressful. • Take short breaks. • Breath, take short exercise – power naps. • Relax often.

What other changes would you like to make in your life? What changes are possible today in your present situation. Remember the point of power is always in the present moment.

Exercise 10

My suggestions of changes I would like to make in my life at this time
Home/personal • • •   Work • • •

HELP FROM THE OUTSIDE

In addition to the relaxation exercises already discussed there are available a host of disciplines and therapies which may be helpful to you at certain times. Learning a particular discipline increases your skills for coping with life. Availing of one of the many therapies available may be appropriate at times to help reduce accumulated stress or to deal with issues that need professional assistance and guidance.

Yoga

Yoga is a body and mind discipline which involves physical postures that allow the body to stretch gently while massaging internal organs and glands. It also involves breathing exercises. Practising yoga leads to deep relaxation of the mind and body. It helps develop clarity of mind and concentration skills, as well as physical strength and flexibility. Ultimately it can lead to deep spiritual awareness.

Meditation

There are many different forms of meditation. All meditation practises work with the close links between body and mind. One of the aims of meditation is the development of harmony between body and mind. In meditation one endeavours to empty the conscious mind and to transcend the busyness of the everyday world. Regular practise of meditation leads to peace and harmony within the person and enhances the way they relate to everyday living. It may also lead to spiritual awareness.

Tai Chi

Tai Chi is a martial art. It is a meditation in and through movement. Slow and deliberate movement together with conscious breath are used to bring the body into balance. The regular practise of Tai Chi leads to the person being grounded and centred.

Autogenics
Autogenics is a relaxation technique which uses the parasympathetic nervous system to turn off the fight or flight reaction. It is a non-confrontative technique which involves to use of the person's imagination to bring about stress release and the induction of the relaxation state.

The Alexander technique
The Alexander technique helps to correct physiological conditions by teaching people to hold their bodies correctly. By developing the correct alignment of the body it is possible to eliminate many of the causes of pain and ill-health. Improving the body posture leads to improved health.

Massage
The ancient art of massage is experiencing a welcome return in the West. There are many types of therapeutic massage all of which greatly enhance the body's capacity to relax. Swedish massage, intuitive massage and aromatherapy massage are widely available now. All forms of massage are deeply relaxing, ease muscle tension and relive tiredness, allowing the life energy to flow freely again. Aromatherapy massage in addition involves the use of essential oils from plants and herbs. Some of these essential oils function as bactericidal, antifungal or antiviral agents. Other oils are relaxing, uplifting, balancing, calming and revitalising. The oils work with and enhance the body's natural metabolic processes.

Acupressure and shiatsu
Both of these body therapies are somewhat similar to acupunture using finger pressure in place of needles. This pressure applied to specific points on the body stimulate or sedate and bring balance to the flow of life energy (often referred to as Ch'i) along the energy channels or meridians

in the body. Both acupressure and shiatsu can be used to bring relief to a wide variety of physical illness.

Reflexology
Reflexology is a widely available and very popular therapy. It is a type of foot massage. It is based on the idea that the feet are a map of the body and have reflex points relating to each organ or body structure. Therefore, by treating the feet we indirectly treat the whole body system. It is deeply enjoyable and relaxing.

Counselling and psychotherapy.
It is sometimes necessary to get outside help with the mental or emotional problems we are experiencing. This is no longer considered something to feel ashamed about. There are many different types of counselling available including those which deal specifically with depression, anxiety, incest, sexual abuse and marital difficulties. Be sure to find the type of therapy that suits your needs – you may have to experience a few before you find one that is right for you. Finally:

Take time
Take time to think – it is the source of power.
Take time to read – it is the foundation of wisdom.
Take time to play – it is the secret of staying young.
Take time to be quiet – it is the opportunity to seek God.
Take time to be aware – it is the opportunity to help others.
Take time to love and be loved – it is God's greatest gift.
Take time to laugh – it is the music of the soul.
Take time to be friendly – it is the road to happiness.
Take time to dream – it is what the future is made of.
Take time to pray – it is the greatest power on earth.
Take time to give – it is too short a day to be selfish.
Take time to work – it is the price of success.

(Source Unknown)

Chapter 5

Constructing a future

We each have the capacity in every moment of our lives to create hell or heaven on earth. This capacity depends to some extent on the way we think. Everything that now exists began as a thought or idea in somebody's mind; therefore thinking is a powerful tool. From our thinking we create much of our own reality. This does not in any way negate the influences of outside events on the construction of our lives. Most of us find that life constantly challenges us to an adventure, throwing as it does unexpected events along our way. Whether we see the unexpected as opportunity or as problem depends to a certain extent on our mind-set and our thinking. If you are a person who needs to be in control of all the external circumstances and the outcome of all events in life then you will not welcome the unplanned, you will not easily deviate from your previously arranged course of action, and for you life's unexpectedness will be very stressful. If you are the type of person who is less attached to a preconceived outcome from events you will find it easier to adapt to changing circumstances and no doubt will thrive on the challenges offered by many of life's unexpected turn of events.

HEALTHY MINDS

So how is it with you and your mind? Is your mind calm and serene and filled with positive images at least some of the time? Or is it constantly agitated and berating you with negative thoughts of 'what if'? Do you consider your mind to be a healthy and life giving resource for you? Does your mind and its activity drain your life energy and add to your general lack of well being? When we speak about health how often do we include mental health? What are the characteristic that distinguish a healthy mind from an unhealthy one?

An unhealthy mind is one that is in constant turmoil always nattering or being a slave to repetitive thoughts, many of which are negative. An unhealthy mind is often one filled with fear and is mostly closed to new ideas and new ways of doing things. Such a mind provokes stressful responses to many life situations.

Characteristics of a healthy mind:
- The capacity to focus attention on a specific topic without interruption.
- Experience of the full spectrum of thoughts and images both positive and negative.
- An openness which means that it won't be used in a defensive way to close out new insights.
- The ability to insure that it is not a slave to repetitive thoughts.
- The capacity to be creative ie express the new, moving past habitual patterns of thinking.

Just as the body's health depends to some extent on the diet we eat – so also the health of the mind is dependant on the thoughts, ideas, images and possibilities that we feed it. It is important for us to be aware of the damage to the physical body caused by certain foods, so also we need to acknowledge the damage and distress caused to our mental well being when we feed our minds with certain thoughts and belief systems.

REFLECTION ON SELF

The following exercise will help you to examine your mind's health by asking yourself the questions:

Exercise 1

- Do you see the world as a dangerous place?
- Do you see change as a challenge or a threat?
- Do you believe in the essential goodness of people including yourself?
- Do you worry about life (a) sometimes (b) never (c) always?
- Would you describe yourself as anxious?
- Would you describe yourself as happy and successful? How do you define happy or successful?
- Would you consider yourself to be open minded?
- Do you like yourself?
- Do you approve of yourself?
- Do you have good self esteem?

As you explore these questions reflect on where did you get these ideas and belief system? Do they serve you well?

INTEGRATION OF MIND AND BODY

The ideas that we accept as true for us help to create the reality of our lives. Life is not something that happens to us – we have a role in its creation and that role is strongly influenced by our thinking – that is why it is so important to take care with our thoughts.

We each of us are composed of body, mind, emotions and spirit. Each of these aspects has its own separate identity within our lives yet they are not isolated and completely separated from each other. They, in fact, strongly influence each other – the body is influenced by feelings, the feelings by thinking – the body is also influenced by thinking and all of them influence the spirit of life within the person. All feelings have their genesis in the body - so by tuning in to distress in the body we can discover the underlying feelings being experienced and housed in the body. Dyhanni Ywahoo, a friend and teacher, says: 'Our bodies are the temples built with the bricks of our thoughts'. So we and our different parts are constantly interrelating.

I would like to explore the influence of the mind and thinking on the feelings and also the effect of thinking and feelings on the body. It has been extensively demonstrated that negative thinking influences our physical well-being. In particular it has been shown that destructive thoughts suppress the immune system – which is the body's defence mechanism – and leaves us more open to infections. The emotional distress (see Chapter 1) that results from negative thinking is subtle, pervasive and in the long term, extremely debilitating.

Effects of stress on the mind

Much of the experience of feeling down or low or in a negative space comes from our thinking patterns. Exploring the relationship between negative thinking and feelings of inferiority, sadness, anger, depression, guilt and fear will offer the possibility to take more control of our feelings and how they impact on our lives.

Some people may not believe that they can actually change the way they feel in or about a certain situation. That in itself is a belief system that causes a feeling of helplessness, hopelessness and frustration. Feelings of sadness and depression come from thoughts of loss. Feelings of frustration are the result of unfulfilled expectations, anxiety and panic. Excessive worry comes from the feelings of impending danger. Anger is the result of a feeling of unfairness. Feelings of guilt and shame are from a belief that you are not okay – that you are bad. The feelings are a consequence of the belief system or the thoughts we hold about ourselves and the reality of life. Often our thinking is distorted and unhelpful and may be coming from our unexamined past conditioning. This is why it is important to challenge our thinking every so often and to check out 'Is this reality true? Does this belief serve me now? And if it doesn't, can I begin to change the belief so that I can feel more at peace within myself, having a greater degree of contentment and happiness?' Distortions in thinking have been studied extensively by many professional groups. Some of these are described below.

DISTORTED THINKING PATTERNS

Black-and-white thinking: Such thinking is that everything and every situation is either black or white, good or bad. In such thinking absolutes are the reality and such thinkers see themselves as either perfect or a complete failure.

Over-generalisation: This is when a simple negative event is allowed to assume the reality of a general pattern – so you assume that if a bad outcome happens once it will always happen.

Negative filtering: This is when a person looks at a certain situation, filters out or ignores the positive elements and concentrates or focuses on the negative elements only.

'Shoulds': This distorted pattern is when your belief about how you and others need to live is based on 'shoulds' and 'oughts'.

Inappropriate blaming: This is when you either blame yourself or other people inappropriately for the problems you experience.

Emotional reasoning: This is when your beliefs about yourself result from your feelings about yourself. You feel boring, or silly – therefore you must be boring or silly.

Unrealistic expectations of self and others: Characteristics of this type of thinking include:

- You expect others to change to suit you.
- You know what is fair but others don't agree with you.

- You feel you are responsible for the pain and happiness of others around you.
- You expect or hope that your sacrifice will pay off and you are angry resentful when people don't reward you the way you expect them to.

Mind reading and jumping to conclusions: Both these thinking patterns are based on inadequate information. You expend a lot of energy with a situation you believe to be true without checking it out properly with the other parties.

Do you recognise any of these patterns in your own thinking? Perhaps when you are under pressure some of these thinking patterns become more exaggerated. As you explore these thinking patterns ask yourself: 'What can I do to challenge this particular thinking pattern? As a first step see if you can identify which distortion the negative thought you are experiencing fits into. Then you might like to examine the evidence about your thoughts and assumptions and ask yourself: 'Is this true'? Is it completely true? How about evaluating the situation not in terms of all or nothing but on a scale from 0-100? You might also ask yourself what are the advantages and the disadvantages of your negative thoughts? When you have gone through this procedure you may be in a position to modify your original negative thought.

The effect of the past on our present reality

Our present day reality is based in part on our past. We all come out of our history, yet we need not be prisoners of our past or our history. Many of the thoughts which we experience come from the beliefs we hold about the reality of life and many of these have been consciously and unconsciously picked up by us as we journeyed through our lives. They often reflect the thinking and conditioning that formed the basis of our education, both formal and informal. Because our belief systems and our thoughts are so central to our experience of reality and in fact are a key so central to our experience of reality, and in fact are a key in the creation of our reality, it is important that we take care with our thoughts. The human mind has conscious and unconscious components within it, both of which influence the creation of our daily lives — often the greatest influence is exerted by the unconscious component. Its influence can undermine much of our conscious thinking and efforts. For this reason it is important to bring as much as possible of the unconscious into light and consciousness, so that its stealthy effects can be exposed. Much of what lies in the unconscious aspect of the mind comes from negative or painful experiences in our past that caused us to develop certain coping mechanisms and belief systems. These have become so much a part of us that we no longer notice them consciously and so their effect can be very subtle and very undermining. The only way that we can free ourselves from them is to begin the process of examining and questioning them. By doing this we can begin the creation of a new way of being.

Past - present - future

Here are two possible scenarios as we explore the effect of the past on the present and the future:

Table i: Effects of past on present and future

Scenario 1

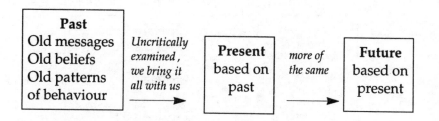

Table J: Effect of past on present and future Scenario 2

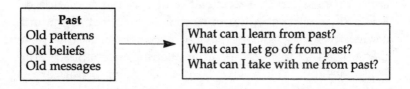

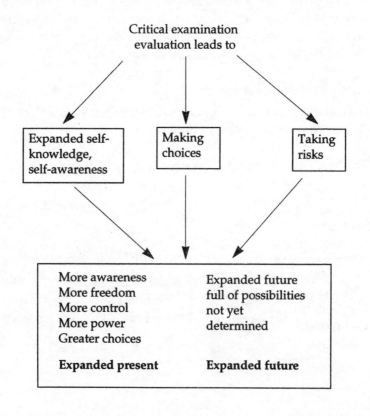

Every cell in our body changes every seven years, yet often our thinking and perception stays the same. In the past we have old messages received and learned from old behaviour/beliefs/patterns. These old messages usually remain with us and are not examined. This, of course, means that we bring them to bear on our present experiences, which ultimately means that if they remain unchallenged and unchanging – our future will always be based on our present.

If we can realise that a critical examination of the old patterns, beliefs, messages and behaviours can lead to awareness, freedom and control, then our present-day life is more empowered and allows us greater choices. This in turn means that our future takes on an expanded nature – and the possibilities are not determined by our present or past. To do this, we need to want expanded self-knowledge and self-awareness, we have to want and be willing to make choices. And, very importantly, we have to be willing to take risks.

The beginning of any critical examination of our past can be with three simple questions asked of each experience/belief pattern:

- What can I learn from the past?
- What can I let go of from the past?
- What can I take with me from the past?

PAST INFLUENCES

In what ways does your past impede you in living your life successfully? So much of past conditioning has become unconscious in us that we need to focus attention on various questions and aspects in order to gain insights into how the past is affecting us at this moment.

Exercise 2

Do the following to raise your self-awareness of the past:
- Do you consider that you are living your life to its full capacity or potential?

- If not what do you think stops you doing that?
- Take a few moments and write out some of the things which you believe stop you from living to your full capacity or potential?
- As you do this exercise be aware of any thoughts and/or feelings that are awakened or evoked in you.
- Make a list.
- As you review this list are there any things that stem from your past conditioning or from beliefs that you inherited as you grew up?

To a large extent the way we live our lives and the behaviours that we engage in come from the beliefs that we hold about ourselves, other people and the reality of life. Many of these beliefs which we picked up from our school, family, church and society, form the basis on which we live our present lives. Some of them are so fundamental in us that we don't consciously think about them or even question their validity. We assume 'this is how life is'.

The problem is that many of the beliefs and ideas we picked up *en-route* in our lives are very negative and cause us much distress. Many of the beliefs that we learned about the reality of life have fear as a central component. Fear generates fear and defensive behaviour results. Much of the defensive behaviour that we engage in causes us a great degree of distress.

Exercise 3
Do the following to examine the fears which cause you distress:
- What fears constantly or occasionally impinge on your capacity to live fully and enjoy life.
- List the fears you experience.

Exercise 4
Do the following to raise self-awareness of past:
- What kind of messages verbal and non verbal did you pick up about the reality of life as you grew up?
- What kind of messages did you receive about yourself as you grew up?

- What negative messages did you hear or receive about yourself and the world when you were a child?
- Take a sheet of paper and take some time to reflect on the messages that you learned as you grew up.
- Recall the belief systems and thinking patterns that you learned, consciously and unconsciously, in your childhood.
- Write them down.
- As you do this exercise notice and observe any feelings or body sensations.
- As you look at this list ask yourself if any of these ideas and belief systems are still forming the basis of your present reality?
- If they do, how do they affect you and your life today?
- Do they serve you well or do they limit you and your life?
- While doing this exercise be careful not to judge yourself but only observe and accept what is true at this time.

SELF ACCEPTANCE AND SELF ESTEEM

Working with many different groups of people from a variety of backgrounds I have become aware of a very common cause of distress in people's lives. The cause is a basic lack of self-esteem and self-acceptance. It is quite amazing how widespread this lack of self acceptance and self-esteem is and how it permeates the lives of so many people in our present society. Often this sense of inadequacy which accompanies the lack of self esteem is deep within the person forming part of their core belief system. It is often extremely well covered up and disguised even from the person themselves. There is a deep-seated core of shame and guilt which leads people to experience themselves as unloveable, as unacceptable, as not really being good enough. These core belief systems lead people into behaviours, and lifestyles that are very distressful.

The myth of perfection

The myth of perfection – the myth that we should know everything and do everything right the first time around causes people to constantly experience themselves as failures. The myth that other people 'they' know everything or do everything right, causes us to compare ourselves unfavourably with others and leaves us experiencing ourselves as failures. The myth that we should be completely integrated and have no flaws is one that constantly undermines our capacity to love and accept ourselves as we are in this moment.

The idea of perfection when perfection is defined as meaning without a flaw or blemish is not an idea that is reflected in the natural world. Did you ever see a tree without a blemish? Our images of perfection tend to come from the Greco-Roman ideas which often find expression in the wonderful forms of the Greek and Roman statues. What is important to remember about those statues is that they are cast in marble and are not alive. Teilhard de Chardin once wrote that: 'to become perfect is to become ever more aware in a world where there is ever more to see'. For me, the important concept in this definition is the concept of becoming. In life we are always engaged in becoming – that is the process of life. We never stop becoming as long as we are alive. This concept is in stark contrast to the concept of 'having arrived' and of seeing perfection as static, once achieved event which when reached, can be maintained. In Teilhaard de Chardin's definition of perfection the word 'perfect' could be replaced by the word 'whole'. In natural living systems perfection in truth is about wholeness. The words 'whole', 'healthy' and 'holy' all have a common root - perhaps this reflects the reality that to be healthy is to be whole. In order for us to be healthy in mind and body we must accept all of who we are and resist the temptation to cut off and disown any aspects of ourselves.

Exercise 5

Do the following to encourage integration:

Owning all of myself

Take a sheet of paper and rule in four sections as outlined below and over. Prepare to complete the following sentences:

- In Section A respond to the statement: *'My parents, teachers and society raised me to be ...'* fill in the qualities that you were raised with in A.
- In Section B write the opposite word to each of the listed qualities in A.
- In Section C respond to the statement: *'As an adult I accept myself when I am ...* in C.
- In Section D fill in the opposite words or phrases that completes the sentence. *'As an adult I need to accept myself more when ...*

When you have completed this exercise you might like to check if there are any similarities between (A) and (C) or (B) and (D).

- If you find that there are similarities what is that saying to you?

(A)	(B)
•	•
•	•
•	•
•	•
•	•

```
(C)          (D)
•            •

•            •

•            •

•            •

•            •
```

The parts of our self that we don't like or can't accept are often referred to as the Shadow. The Shadow is sometimes represented as a bag into which we put those parts of ourselves that are difficult for us to own - these parts may be positive or negative. This bag gets heavier as we fill it with unacceptable parts of ourselves. As it does it weighs us down decreasing our capacity for living fully in this present moment and accepting the reality of who we are. Not accepting all of who we are is a great source of distress in the lives of many people.

GUILT

'Guilt is the gift that keeps on giving' and you might well ask what gifts your guilt gives to you? Before you answer this let us explore the concept of guilt and how it affects our lives.

Healthy guilt

Joan Borysenko, in her book, *Guilt is the Teacher, Love Is the Lesson*, explores the differences between healthy and unhealthy guilt.

Healthy guilt is that which allows us to develop a conscience by providing us with feed back about the effect and consequence of inappropriate or hurtful behaviour. Healthy guilt separates the inappropriate actions from the person involved.

Healthy guilt allows a person to experience a sense of sadness and/or regret about something they may have done without experiencing themselves as bad or worthless.

Unhealthy guilt

Unhealthy guilt comes from a shame based identity where a feeling of shame may be at the very core or centre of what a person believes about themselves. This feeling of shame may translate into a belief such as 'I am a fundamentally flawed human being'. (This is different from the belief that each human being is imperfect but whole that I spoke about earlier). Unhealthy guilt makes a person feel badly about most things, always feeling or thinking that they could have done better. It makes it difficult for people to forgive themselves. It causes a build up of anger and resentment towards themselves and others. Unhealthy guilt leads to a lack of acceptance of certain characteristics and parts of the person. This often results in behaviour whose function is to hide these characteristics from themselves and from others.

Unhealthy guilt is often the root and cause of obsessive and compulsive behaviour in people, because of their need to hide from the feelings of shame and guilt. Unhealthy guilt — accompanied by low self-esteem causes much distress in people's lives. There is often excessive amounts of fear in such people - the fear of being discovered - the fear of not being all right of not measuring up. This guilt and the fear associated with it leads to defensive behaviour which results in a closed type of lifestyle where the central need is to defend the core from exposure. Such a lifestyle results in distress, sadness and lack of joy.

So what can be done about feelings of guilt, fear and low self-esteem? An important factor to remember in this scenario is that feelings are influenced and partly created in response to thoughts and attitudes. The messages that you give yourself, often unconsciously, have a significant

103

effect on your emotions. By changing the thoughts you entertain, and the attitudes you hold about yourself and life, you can change the way you feel. The process of thinking is very central to the creation of reality.

Changing reality
So what kind of thoughts do you feed to your mind? For the next day or two become aware of the negative thoughts that you feed yourself... they might be thoughts that put you down, thoughts, that are fear filled, thoughts that foresee problem outcomes, and a host of others.

Notice the throw-away remarks that you make about yourself. Do they put you down or support you? Each time you notice such a thought or remark; stop. Then observe the negative thought or remark and ask yourself 'How does this thought or remark serve me in this moment?' and ask: 'Is there a different thought that might serve me better?' It is important to remember that your thoughts come from your belief systems – and these are often deeply ingrained and sometimes unconscious.

When you begin this process of challenging thoughts and belief systems you may experience resistance – that is a normal response – the greater the resistance the deeper the belief system and the more it needs to be challenged. When you experience resistance you can be sure you are dealing with issues that need changing!

Expectations and expectancy
Thoughts and belief systems can lead us to certain expectations of ourselves and other people. Expectation are healthy so song as they are realistic. Expectations need to be like the rest of life – not static but fluid. How often do our expectations of ourselves and others lead us to feelings of disappointment and sadness? Would it be better perhaps for us not to have any expectations of ourselves or others? I believe we need to live with the openness and possibilities afforded to us by expectations but we need to hold those expectations lightly – so that they can flow easily with grace and not become a burden on ourselves or

others. One of my teachers used to say that we need to live with 'minimum expectations and maximum expectancy'. So what is the difference, if any, between expectations and expectancy? Expectations are fixed, rigid and static, while expectancy is open, fluid and full of possibilities. So, when we live our lives from a position of expectation we impose limits, rigid structures and ideas about how everything should happen. When it does not happen as we had hoped we feel disappointed, angry, or sad and this can lead us into a spiral of negative thinking and the corresponding negative feelings. What of expectancy? When we live life from a place of expectancy we are open to what may happen, what could happen – we do not have fixed ideas about exactly what needs or should happen – so that we are not easily disappointed with the outcome. We are, in fact, open to what life is offering at the moment and we are responding to that, rather than insisting that life should happen in a certain way and reacting against it when it doesn't.

Do the following exercise to help examine your expectations. One of the great sources of distress in people's lives are the expectations that they place on other people. This exercise can clarify the issues around expectations of self and others and greatly reduce the distress caused by unrealistic expectations.

Exercise 6

- Take a sheet of paper and write on the top *'Nobody has the right to expect me to ...'*
- Then underneath this write out what you think people do not have the right to expect of you.
- Now take another sheet of paper and write over the top *'I don't have the right to expect other people to'* ...
- Fill in underneath this statement what you do not have the right to expect from other people.
- As you look at these two lists what do you notice?

There are of course things that people do have the right to expect from us and that we have the right to expect from others.

- Create two more lists :
  'People have the right to expect me to ...'
  'I have the right to expect other people to ...'

These exercises can be used any time you need to clarify issues concerning expectations.

What are the expectations that you place on yourself? Are they realistic given who you are in this moment and the circumstances of your life at this time? Are your expectations unrealistic and based on inaccurate self-knowledge? If you lack accurate and honest ideas about yourself is it because you haven't fully explored who you are or is it because you refuse to accept certain parts of yourself and try to hide them from yourself and others.

Do you ever think if she/he really knew me they wouldn't or couldn't love or accept me? Do your expectations of yourself come from a need to be approved of by others or to be approved of by yourself? Do you find it easy to accept and approve of yourself? Do these expectations serve you well? Do they contribute to your well-being, your happiness? If not, what is to be gained by holding onto them and even more importantly, what might be gained by letting them go?

How would your life be different if you lived it from a place of self-acceptance and self-love? Self-love and self-acceptance are the foundations on which healthy growth, change and personal fulfilment can be developed.

As you explore these issues you may experience feelings of anger, blame and a sense that past circumstances of your life are responsible for your present situation. This is most unhelpful because in doing so you remain a victim of your past and so do not take responsibility for the present.

So what can you do? In order for anyone to move on and live more fully and with more joy in each moment we need to release those elements of the past that no longer serve us, we need to forgive the past – we need to forgive ourselves and other people so that we can be set free. We need to let go of any resentments we are holding because ultimately they poison our bodies and our minds. Remember, you need to forgive your enemies for your own mental health.

FORGIVENESS

Forgiveness is an essential aspect of healthy living. Yet forgiveness is often very difficult for us to either give or accept. We often think of forgiveness in terms of letting people off the hook – or of stepping down about an issue. We see ourselves in conflictional situations as either the victim or the oppressor. This way of seeking forgiveness means that we always remain in the position of one-up or one-down with the other person. In order to be able to forgive more easily we need to move away from seeing issues in such black-and-white terms. We need to see that we and the other person are together involved in co-creating a situation and that each of us has shared responsibility. We need to realise that when we don't forgive somebody, we stay stuck in the past, a vicious cycle of action and reaction. Lack of forgiveness keeps us locked in our past. By developing an attitude of forgiveness towards ourselves and other people, we become happier, more serene and more compassionate, as we release the need to constantly judge ourselves and everyone else.

Exercise 7
Forgiving another person
- Find a quiet space, take a few deep breaths to centre yourself, exhaling as deeply as possible. When you are centred ask yourself: 'Who do I need to forgive at this time and for what do I need to forgive them?'
- Spend some time with these questions and when you are ready, write down the person's name and what you need to forgive them for – there may be more than one issue and more than one person.
  Continue to do this for as long as necessary.

Now write:
- I forgive you_____for_____
          (name)   (issue)

I release the bonds between us.

- Now, imagine this person accepting your forgiveness and thanking you – and both of you being set free.

Do this exercise, regularly so as to prevent a build up of resentment impinging on your present life.

Exercise 8

Asking forgiveness from another person

- Who are the people you have hurt? Who are the people you may need to ask for forgiveness?
- Spend a few minutes considering this.
- When you are ready write down the names of the people whom you need to ask for forgiveness.
- Write also the issues involved.
- Now imagine that person forgiving you and you accepting the forgiveness and the bonds of resentment held between you being released.

Exercise 9

Self-forgiveness

Sometimes it is difficult for us to forgive ourselves. We feel ashamed or guilty about some behaviour of ours. We cut ourselves off from our own love, we withhold love and acceptance from ourselves. Developing an attitude of self-forgiveness will allow us to become more compassionate towards ourselves. What do you need to forgive yourself for at this time?

- Take a few moments to reflect and then write:

I_____forgive myself for_____

Remember forgiveness is not about condoning behaviour but about letting go and about accepting what is. Accepting what is allows us to live in an honest relationship with ourselves.

RESENTMENT

Part of the journey towards an attitude of forgiveness involves owning, accepting and dealing with resentment that we may feel towards ourselves or other people. Resentment is perhaps one of the greatest sources of suffering and distress that we can experience. Dissolving resentments can greatly improve the quality of life.

Exercise 10
- List some resentments that you are holding, against yourself or other people. As you write each one down be aware of your feelings – Be aware of your body, its posture – the experiences within your body.
- Look at each one – ask yourself, what is the value of holding on to this particular resentment? How does it affect my life? Does it add to my positive well-being? If it doesn't what benefits do I receive from holding on to it? What would be the consequences of letting it go?
- Spend a little time imagining yourself doing something about the issue which is causing your resentment and/or letting go of the resentment. Notice your thoughts, feelings and body sensations as you do this. Allow yourself to be aware of all that you experience.
- In the light of this reflection what step would you like to take to deal with the issues causing the resentment?
- Are there some resentments you might like to release or let go of? If so then write out the steps you will take in each case and also write:

I_____(name) release the resentment that I am holding towards_____for_____
    I now free myself and the other person from the burden of this resentment.

Forgiveness, dissolving resentments and letting go of the past are key factors in creating for ourselves and others a healthier, happier and less stressful future.

Chapter 6

Change and growth

When we find ourselves chronically over-stressed it is a sign that we have stopped paying attention to, and are out of touch with, our true selves. It is a sign that we are not listening to our deep inner self but that we are operating from excessive pressures which we allow ourselves and other people to place on us. Many of these pressures ignore the reality of who we are and of what is possible and they operate from a place of 'should'. Living one's life from a place of 'should' leads to self-deception and a lack of awareness of how one really is at any time. Living without awareness causes all of us much unnecessary distress.

Self-awareness is the key that allows us to know who we are; it is the opposite of self-deception. We are, each of us, self-deceived when our 'shoulds' so dominate us they blind our awareness of present realities. Embracing the reality of life involves a commitment to self-exploration and self-observation and a pursuit of clear insight which allows us to cut through the illusions and deceptions that often distorts our reality. The resulting increase in self-awareness allows us at each moment to make choices which are more suitable personally for us. Deliberately making choices in this way allows each of us to take more personal responsibility for ourselves and our lives. As we do this we experience our power and see ourselves more as actors than reactors to our life.

The commitment to self-exploration and self-observation is not meant to be an obsessive effort, nor is it meant to be done in a spirit of judgement or criticism. In fact, in order for it to be useful, it must be done in a non-judgmental and non-critical way - since criticism interferes with learning and growth. Non-critical observation and acceptance of ourselves allows us to notice our behaviour. Observing our reactions to certain issues allows us to explore the belief systems and the thought patterns that underpin our behaviour. Sometimes we need to step to one side of ourselves and observe ourselves as if we were a researcher. Examining our behaviour in this detached way allows us to ask questions like 'Does this response or reaction to that event, serve me well'? Does it work for me in this moment? Asking these questions can lead to a greater degree of choice in the way we respond to any event. Only by understanding our values, our beliefs and our attitudes and how they translate into choices and behaviours can we progress to making new and more satisfying choices. Knowing who we really are is a powerful experience. Naming, owning and accepting who we are allows us the freedom that comes with truth. Denial keeps us in a state of disempowerment. Knowing and accepting who we are, in any moment, is one of the keys to growth and change.

IS THE FUTURE MORE OF THE SAME?

'If you don't like where you are headed you had better change direction or you will end up where you are headed'. This Chinese adage has a powerful message for anyone who is wondering about their future and how it might unfold. At workshops I frequently ask people 'Do you like where you are in your life? Do you like the direction your life is headed in?'

The most common response to these questions is no. When these questions are further explored it often emerges that many people believe that one can't really expect too much from life, one certainly can't expect the future to be very different from the past. How do you see the future unfolding?

111

- Will it be similar to the past — will it be different?
- Would you like it to be different?
- How would you like it to be different?
- Take a few moments to reflect on these questions.
- It might be helpful for you to write out your answers.

As you reflect on your answers, assuming there are some changes and differences you would like to create in the future, ask yourself: how can I go about this? What must I do to bring about the changes I desire? Returning to the Chinese adage — you will notice that the advice offered is to change direction if you don't like where you are headed. For a moment picture yourself on a road going somewhere. You suddenly realise that you are on the wrong road or on a road headed somewhere other than you intended. You decide to change direction.

The decision to change direction comes from a realisation that you are somewhere other than where you wish to be. It comes from an acceptance of this fact rather than from any attempt to deny it. This illustrates that change is only possible by an acceptance of 'what is'. This is the paradox: if you want to change anything then the first step in the process is to accept what now exists. Real change needs accurate self-knowledge which requires openness, honesty and trust in yourself and in life. Most people approach the change from a perspective of 'I should' and it is because of this that so many people fail to bring about the changes they say they would like to. Approaching change from an 'I should' perspective is to guarantee failure because it comes from a place of non-acceptance and of judgement against yourself. 'Should' is a product of the ego and of the mind — it is closely associated with the internal critic and it is often associated with the false self rather than the true self and with external rather than internal values. The false self is the one we sometimes show to the public — the self we feel we have to be. The true self, is as its name implies, is the self that more fully reflects who we really are. This is why it is extremely

difficult to effectively bring about change using the mind
set 'should'.

FINDING THE POINT OF POWER

Perhaps you are thinking if I don't use 'should' against
myself how will I ever change or improve? I would like to
offer you another way of approaching the idea of personal
growth and change. It is an approach based on the key
words and concepts of awareness, choice and
responsibility. Earlier I explored the issue of awareness
and its importance in this process. Developing the capacity
to make choices is partly based on awareness and partly on
developing an internal value system, together with the
willingness to accept responsibility for the outcome of the
decisions. This requires self discipline and the use of the
will. The will is the ability to find ones own law inside
oneself and be willing to follow that law. It is not the same
as will power which is often rigid and judgmental. Self
discipline is seen as doing not what I want to do but what I
deeply and truly need to do. All of these concepts point
towards living from the inside out. To making decisions
and choices based on a degree of inner freedom. Each time
we make choices and take responsibility for our choices we
empower ourselves and we move away from the position
of victim towards the position of empowered person.

It is amazing to realise that in each moment of our lives
we have choices and that each choice taken leads to certain
consequences. The choices we make in this moment are
shaping our future because the future is being created by
the way we live now. So, each present moment is very
important - no moment can ever be underestimated
because each offers us an opportunity for growth and
development and change. So often we procrastinate to say
'I'll begin to change tomorrow' or 'next year' - that in itself
is a choice with consequences. This present moment is the
only one we have or are sure about - the past moment is

gone and the future moment has not yet arrived. This present moment is the only one that we can act upon, which is why it is said that the point of power is always in this present moment.

Beginning to live life from this perspective may initially cause us concern or a feeling of being burdened with responsibility. Having to deal with the idea of making choices and decisions and living with the consequences of these choices may appear to be too great a responsibility. But with each decision that is taken and each choice freely made, you become more involved in the way your life unfolds. You become a co-creator in your own reality. This leads to a sense of being empowered – that is, being in touch with the power within yourself. Responsibility in this context is not a burden but is in fact one's ability to respond. As a person becomes more aware of themselves and their behaviour, makes changes and decisions, they are better able to respond to the circumstances of their lives and so live more responsibly.

FROM VICTIM TO EMPOWERED PERSON

One of the important journeys or transitions that we are invited to make during our lifetime is the journey from victim to empowered person. It is a journey that occurs with many steps and stages. Often people respond to the outside events of their lives with 'why did this have to happen to me?' Choosing this response is to choose the role of victim – to experience oneself as not in control. Choosing to respond to an outside event with: 'This has happened and I choose to respond to it in this way,' or 'What can I learn from this?' is to choose the role of empowered person. An empowered person knows that real power lies within themself and that it is related to the capacity to make choices and take responsibility for their outcome. Often we allow ourselves to be victims of other people and we express this as 'he/she made me really angry'. When we do this we are not taking responsibility for our part in the interaction – we are believing that the other person has the power to make us angry and that we are victims of that power. A person acting from a position of power within themselves would recognise the fact 'that when the person did x their response was anger'. They would also admit that other choices could have been made which would have resulted in different outcomes.

WHAT IS IT LIKE TO CONSCIOUSLY CHOOSE?

In every moment of our lives we have choices. Sometimes the choices are not very obvious, sometimes the choices are not easy, but they are always there and available to us. The following exercise allows you the experience of consciously making choices.

Exercise 1
- Take a moment to settle yourself wherever you are now.
- Focus your mind for a moment on the idea of choice.
- Look around the space you are in (room, house, garden, office, shop).
- As you explore this space, what are the things that you could do here and now?
- List them either in your head or write them down.
- Now choose one of these things and go and do it – reflect on how that felt.
- Now consider again all the possible things you could do and this time open up your awareness of what is going on inside as you do. Notice how your body is – what thoughts are going through your mind? How do you feel? What is happening as you consciously choose?
- Now choose another activity and observe what happens to you as you make the choice – now carry out the activity.
- Again reconsider all the possible choices of activity.
- Pick another one and this time choose not to do it. Be aware of how that is for you.
- So how is the experience of making choices?

(This exercise is adapted from an exercise by Diana Whitmore in Psychosynthesis in Education, Turnstone Press 1986.)

SHOULD AND COULD

If ever there was a word that caused pain, guilt, distress and much hardship in the lives of people it is the word 'should'. We constantly berate ourselves with what we should do and each time we do this we rob ourselves of the opportunity to use our will wisely. The following exercise explores and allows you to experience the difference between could and should.

Exercise 2
This exercise is in four parts.

Part 1
Take a sheet of paper and write in big letters across the top '*I should_____*

_____

Beneath this write down all the things that you constantly tell yourself that you should do.
• As you do this be aware of your feelings.
• How do you feel as you write down all these 'shoulds'?

Part 2
• Take another sheet of paper and write in big letters across the top '*If I really wanted to I could*'
• Now write in all the things from the 'I should list' above.
• Pick out one of these and read it out loud or to yourself, eg '*If I really wanted to I could get up earlier in the morning*'.
• Pause for a moment and respond '*Yes I could and I have a choice.*'
• Repeat this for all the statements on this list.
• How does it feel to do this?
• How is this experience different from the experience of 'I should'?

Part 3
- Go back to the 'should' list.
- Read out each one again pausing after you have read it and ask yourself: why should I?
- Then write your response to each one.
- Study your responses - what insights do they offer you?

Part 4
- Now look at the list *'If I really wanted to I could'*.
- Read each one to yourself or out loud then gently ask yourself 'Why haven't I'?
- Now write down the responses.
- Study all the responses in each part of the exercise and ask yourself 'What, if anything, is all of this information saying to me?'
- In the light of these insights create a new list of things that you would like to do, omit or include in your life.

Based on exercises in Louse Hay, *You can Heal Your Life* and Diana Whitworth, *Psychosynthesis in Education*.

GROWTH AND UNFOLDING

Growth and unfolding, it appears, is something that happens without conscious effort in the natural world. The final outcome of the growth will be influenced by circumstances in the environment but essentially a rose seed becomes a rose bush, a pear seed becomes a pear tree and an acorn becomes an oak tree. What of us humans? What will we unfold into or become in this lifetime? Animals and plants to a large extent live out a destination but human beings shape their destination. One of the very distinctive characteristics of human beings is the capacity to influence their evolution through awareness and choice. Co-creation is a unique human ability and challenge.

The capacity to make decisions and choices

differentiates the human growth process from others in the natural world. Human growth when balanced and healthy develops in all directions and involves all aspects of the person, body, mind, emotions and spirit. To grow and develop is to move past where one is at a certain time, to let go the limits of that particular perception of oneself and the world and to move towards a larger more inclusive view of oneself and the world. Such growth involves the risk of moving from where there is a certain degree of familiarity and security to places that may be unfamiliar.

As you reflect on where you are at this moment in your life you may identify aspects of yourself or your life that you would like to develop, change or encourage to grow. If so the following steps might help.

Steps towards growth

- Sort out what it is you wish to change or develop.
- List all the things you feel you can't change then list the ones you feel you can change.
- Pick from this list one or two that you will actively work on at this time.
- Accept your situation exactly as it is at this time.
- Imagine or visualise the change you would like to see happen, focusing your attention on it often.
- Develop an awareness of your thinking and behavioural patterns that may stop you changing or growing or be a cause of the situation that you are in.
- Look at the gifts that you have that will help you with this chosen change.
- Pick small steps — note and celebrate your successes.
- Notice the times you couldn't do it and forgive yourself.
- Use these 'failures' as opportunities to learn about yourself by asking: 'What was it about that situation that made it difficult?'
- Reinforce in yourself the idea that you have the courage, the commitment and the will to change.
- Write affirmations about the desired change or growth and note your response.
- Be aware of your resistance to change.

- Acknowledge the resistance and choose to change anyway!

Since the reality of life is systemic — that is, life is an interconnected system, then when one aspect or part changes it affects all of the system. That is important and encouraging because it means that when we change one aspect of our life then our whole life changes.

AFFIRMATIONS

To affirm something means to make it firm or certain. When I speak about making affirmations as a tool to help growth I am referring to the use of positive affirmations, so, using affirmations involves making strong positive statements about what I would like to happen. It is always best to make affirmations in the present tense rather than in the future tense because it allows us to connect with the power of the present moment.

Affirmations can be spoken silently or out loud or they can be written, depending on your own preference at different times. When writing affirmations it is very useful to also write the negative responses that jump into your mind as soon as you have said the affirmation. That is often your resistance to change, so you might like to use this method.

Exercise 3
- Take a sheet of paper, draw a line down the middle.
- Write the affirmation on the left-hand side and the negative response on the right-hand side.
- Continue to write the affirmation and each time write whatever response comes into your mind.
- You may find that the resistance decreases and the statements on the right-hand side become more positive.

It is very important that the affirmation that you choose is one that suits you, so spend some time creating the affirmations that might be helpful. I include some that might act as catalysts.

119

The universe is abundant - there is plenty for all of us.

- I am now attracting loving and happy relationships into my life.
- I am an open channel of creative energy.
- I communicate clearly and effectively.
- I attract to myself all that I need at this moment.
- I am a loveable and worthy person at this moment.
- I give with joy and receive with joy.
- All my needs are being perfectly met now.
- I now accept all my feelings as part of myself.
- I accept myself exactly as I am.
- I accept myself completely as I am and I am open to growing.
- I now release worn-out objects, worn-out ideas and worn-out relationships.
- I free myself from the burden of blaming other people.
- I take full responsibility for my life now.
- I now create the circumstances needed for me to grow and change.

RESISTANCE TO CHANGE AND GROWTH

One thing that you can be sure of is that when you begin to change and grow you will encounter resistance and opposition. The resistance and opposition will come from yourself and from other people, because when you change others will experience the consequence of the change and they might have to change also. Both of these sources need to be acknowledged and taken seriously, but must not be allowed to interfere with your decision to grow and change. Resistance to change comes in all kinds of guises, many of which are extremely plausible and some are even laudable. You need to be aware of what forms your own resistance takes. What does your resistance look like? Some common resistances are listed below — they will help you to recognise your own patterns of resistance to the process of change.

Common resistances:

- Procrastination 'As soon as I get ... then I'll do it':
  Eating
  Drinking
  Changing the subject

- Making statements to ourselves or others like:
  It would not do any good.
  My partner wouldn't approve.
  My partner wouldn't understand.
  My situation is different.
  Spiritual people would do that.
  Spiritual people don't get angry.
  I can't afford it.
  I don't want to hurt them.

- It may also be ideas about ourselves like:
  I'm too old.
  I'm too young.
  I'm too fat.
  I'm too thin.
  I'm too intelligent.
  I'm too stupid.

FACING FEAR

Fear is the biggest source of resistance. Some fears may be:
  They might reject me.
  What would they say if they knew?
  I'm afraid I would not be good enough.
  I don't want to open up that issue.
People often feel afraid and insecure in fully pursuing the changes they desire. Fear is the single biggest obstacle to growth and change. Fear can paralyse anyone at any time. So what can be done about this fear? You must challenge the fear and you must do it while you are still afraid. A friend of mine used to say 'the other side of the coin fear is freedom but you must go through the fear to experience the freedom.' You must go into your fear because in it you

will experience your power to overcome it. We need to realise that we have everything we need to live life fully and that includes what is needed to overcome our fears.

Finally, I would like you to consider how you would like to be in two- or five- or ten-years time. How would you like someone to describe you?

Exercise 4

Allow yourself time and space where you will not be interrupted. Take a few moments, focus your attention on your breathing and use your breath to bring you into your centre.

- Exhale deeply and as you relax close your eyes and ask yourself: 'How would I like to be in two, five or ten years?' Choose the time-span that is right for you.
- Spend a few minutes with this question and when you are ready open your eyes and write your response in as much detail as possible.
- Close your eyes again and ask yourself: 'What do I need to let go of in order for this to happen?'
- Reflect on this and when you are ready write your response.
- Close your eyes and ask yourself: 'What do I need to hold on to in order for this to become a reality?'
  When you are ready write your response.
- Now close your eyes again and ask yourself: 'What obstacles am I likely to put in my own way?'
  When you are ready write your response.
- Finally, what step or steps can you take, however small, in the next 24 hours as first steps towards reaching that goal?
- Again when you are ready write your response.
- Now write:

'I_____affirm my willingness to take step_____and to begin the journey toward becoming what I wish to become.

Now you are truly on your journey to self-awareness, change and development.

(This exercise is adapted from one I learned from Jean Lanier).

Chapter 7

Conflict resolution

Conflict and its resolution, especially when the resolution is ineffective, is a major source of distress in the lives of people. Many of the problems that occur in the myriad of different relationships that make up the reality of our lives are due to the ineffective resolution of conflict. How often do you think 'Yes, I have myself together and know where I am going. I know how to achieve certain things. If only I didn't have the interference of other people, if only I didn't have to contend with other people and their issues then my life would work well!' While such thoughts may appear to be valid and reasonable, they are in fact not possible – even if they are desirable!

The reality of life is relationships – we are part of the web of life – nothing that lives can exist outside of that web. When you consider the image of the web you see that it is made up of many connecting strands all interconnected with each other – the reality of the web of life is relationship.

Communication
Relationships are fundamental to our lives. We have many different types of relationship – intimate, business, familial and casual, all of which involve us in different ways and engage us in different dynamics. One common thread that runs through all relationships is communication. In order for a relationship to exist there must be communication between the people involved. The type of relationship one has with a person influences in some way the type of communication engaged in with that person. The type of

communication that one engages in is a very significant factor in determining the type of relationship that unfolds with people. It is true to say that bad communication results in difficult, unhealthy relationships while good communication leads to open and healthy relationships.

All communication skills are learned – we each learned the art of communication from those around us as we grew up. If you discover that your type of communication in a certain situation is unhelpful or creating difficulties, it is good to know that since your communication style has been learned it can also be unlearned or a new style learned. However, unlearning can be difficult. What is the difference between good communication and bad communication? Before defining good or bad communication it is important to state that communication not only involves speaking or talking but also listening, and that communication has a non-verbal component as well as a verbal one and sometimes involves what is not overtly expressed.

When good communication happens a person expresses their feelings openly and directly and acknowledges the other person's feelings. Good communication is clear and suitable. When bad communication happens the person does not express feelings openly, does not acknowledge how the other person is thinking or feeling. Instead, the person argues and becomes defensive. Bad communication consists of the unsuitable transferred message.

Relating to ourselves

Our relationships with other people are partly influenced by our relationship with ourselves. How we relate to other people, how we communicate with them is largely influenced by the view we have of ourselves and the world around us. The more at peace I am with myself – the more I can accept the reality of who I am in this moment – the less I need to be defensive in the way I relate to other people. The more centred I am within myself the less I need to fear other people and their possible rejection of me or anything I say or do. When a person experiences low self-esteem, feels badly about who they are or feels they are not good enough they tend to be defensive and closed in their communication with others. If a person experiences low self-esteem then being wrong about something will be a major issue striking them at the core of their being. People like this often perceive differences as threatening and feel most uncomfortable when their views are challenged. People with low self-esteem often feel uncomfortable around conflict and tend to respond to it by either fighting it aggressively or avoiding it entirely. Either or both of these tactics/responses to conflict will lead to bad communication strategies and ultimately to a deterioration of the relationship.

Dynamics of communication

All communication is learned – so what kind of lessons did you learn and internalise about communications as you grew up?

Exercise 1

Ask yourself the following questions:

- How did the significant people in your life communicate with each other and with you?
- Was the communication open and free or was it closed and defensive?
- How did the communications deal with issues of conflict?
- Were you and others given clear, direct messages?
- Did people listen?
- Was the communication respectful?
- Was blame, judgement or martyrdom a feature of the communication?
- Was sarcasm used to communicate displeasure?
- Was there sometimes a dynamics of defensive and counter-attack in the way people communicated with each other?
- Did people around you slam doors or storm out of rooms during rows?
- Did the issues get resolved or did they get swept under the carpet?

- Did the type of communication used help people to develop openness in their relationships?
- Did people get more closed and say 'what is the use'?
- Did people try to get even in subtle ways?
- Was it important to always be right?

As you reflect on these questions ask yourself — have you internalised and brought into your own life any of these common strategies? Do you use them in your communication style, especially in moments of conflict?

What is communication about?

Communication involves listening as well as speaking. There are several types of listening skills all of which enhance the quality of communication. Good listening skills allow the person who is speaking to know that they have been heard, it allows them to clarify their thoughts. It is an extremely important skill and very often is the thing which allows another person to grow and change. The non-verbal aspect of communications involves body language, voice intonation, facial expressions and other nuances which when picked up by the listener allows a more accurate and sensitive response and so a better quality of communication.

All the words a person speaks are messages and codes that translate in a tangible way the thoughts and feelings that occur inside. We are in some sense living inside our skin and talking is an attempt to communicate to the outside world what is happening inside ourselves. Sometimes we communicate this in a clear and direct way and sometimes we don't. The less controversial the topic of communication is, the easier it is for us to be clear and direct. If the communication involves self-disclosure a person may feel fearful about being open. If the communication involves a conflictional issue the way in which we will communicate will depend to a large extent on our views about conflict or confrontation. It will also be influenced by how we view ourselves in the situation and what personal issues it may bring up for us?

Direct communication: Mary feels hungry while at a meeting with Joan. Mary says to Joan 'I am hungry – when will we be eating?' Joan hears that Mary is hungry. This is direct communication.

Indirect communication: Mary feels hungry while at a meeting with Joan. Mary says to Joan 'What time is lunch at in this place?' or 'Is there a canteen here?' Joan may hear that Mary is indirectly saying she is hungry or Joan hears Mary making enquiries about the time lunch is served or if there is a canteen? This is indirect communication.

Direct communication ensures a higher probability of the person hearing exactly what you wish to communicate and also that the needs communicated can be attended to. The experience of fear is one of the biggest obstacles to open and direct communication. Whether it is fear of self-disclosure, fear of disapproval, fear of rejection or fear of being undermined, the fear leads to a position of defensiveness and closeness. Good communication can't happen when people close down. When fear is an issue in a relationship the communication between the people involved becomes unclear and indirect. The problem then arises because the unclear and indirect communication decreases the chances of needs being met. This in turn decreases the level of trust and increases the fear and decreases again the openness of communication. This vicious cycle can only be broken when someone chooses to take the risk involved in breaking out of the cycle by changing the dynamic of the communication pattern.

Conflict and its resolution

What does the word 'conflict' mean to you? What images or memories does the word 'conflict' evoke in you? Most people view conflict as something bad, and to be avoided. Conflict is most often associated with the misuse of power and the struggle for control. Yet perhaps this is not the only way to relate to the idea of conflict. Conflict is a natural part of life. All growth involves the conflict between the urge to move on, to progress, and the urge to stay the same. Without the resolution of this conflict there would be little progress and no real changes, life would be more static and less colourful! What of conflict at a personal level – between people? For many of us it is difficult to believe that conflict can be good and that our relationship can be stimulated and grow through the effective resolution of conflict. Our attempts to suppress conflict or to avoid it in fact contribute enormously to our difficulties with it. When conflict is suppressed it doesn't go away, it just stays under the surface and affects all the subsequent interactions. If we recognised the reality of conflict and the need for its effective resolution, we would spend time developing and learning appropriate methods with which to do this.

Conflicts between people usually fall into one of two categories – conflicts of values and conflicts of needs. Conflict of values are more difficult to resolve, however in most relationships conflicts of needs are the most common type experienced. Conflict can be viewed as a statement of needs not being met by one or several persons in a relationship. Most often however, conflict is viewed as a power struggle and is experienced in terms of winning and losing.

Communication is a key element in the resolution of conflict – again we need to explore the question, 'What does my communication portray in this instant? Is it openness and acceptance or is it judgement and hostility?' The way that people communicate during conflict reflects much of their actual thinking around conflict. When I can view or see conflict as someone's needs not being met – then my communication will be more likely to be open and accepting than if I see conflict as a power struggle, where the communication will tend to be judgmental and confrontational. The idea that conflict can be other than a 'win/lose' situation may be new to most people. With a win/lose model of resolution the possible scenarios are 'you win – I lose', or 'you lose – I win'.

This type of resolution involves the use of power in a way often referred to as 'power over'. It usually involves inequality or perceived inequality in the relationship, the power is seen to be held by one person and it is perceived that that person will use it to get their way.

When conflict is resolved using this model, one or both persons may experience a sense of loss. One person has their needs met at the expense of another. But even though they appear 'to win', in the long-term, they don't really get their needs met because they experience resentment from the other person. The one who appears 'to lose' may feel downhearted and resentful because they never get their needs met. The uncommunicated and unresolved resentments are brought into the next communication and this leads to a decrease in the level of openness and trust between the people, and ultimately to a dead or unhealthy relationship. In order to move away from this model of conflict resolution one must change the belief that conflict is about power struggles, and become open to the idea that conflict in a relationship is a communication about unmet needs. With this belief it is possible to speak of conflict resolution in no-loser terms. In this case the conflict is resolved in such a way that nobody loses.

EFFECTIVE RESOLUTION

Conflict and its effective resolution sometimes requires that we deal with it by confrontation of the issues. This needs to be done in a clear and assertive way without being aggressive. Many people fear and avoid the idea of confrontations in the same way as they do conflicts. What images, positive and negative, does the idea of confrontation evoke in you?

Confronting a person or an issue does not need to be a negative experience. Confrontation involves adopting an active stance and taking responsibility for moving the process along in a way that may result in you getting your needs met and ultimately the other person getting their needs met also. A problem only arises when the ineffective then the problem or the issue remains unresolved and the relationship with the person or group may deteriorate. This can lead to a negative spiral of events in which the situation gets worse.

What causes a confrontation to be ineffective?

Usually the confrontation will be ineffective if the problem is unclearly stated or stated in a manner which blames or judges harshly. It usually employs 'you messages'. Therefore the first step in effective confrontation is to state the problem clearly. The second step is to state the problem or issue using 'I messages' rather than *'you messages'. What is an 'I message'? An I message has three components:

- it tells the person with whom we wish to communicate what the problem is.
- it identifies the concrete effect that the issue or problem is having on us.
- it states the feelings generated within the affected person.

'I messages' can be considered as actions in which the person sending them takes responsibility for their own inner condition and is open enough to communicate this. It also leaves responsibility for the other person's behaviour with them. 'I messages' create a real possibility for the conflict or problem to be resolved. 'I messages' result in relationships being enhanced.

Examples of 'I messages'

The following are examples of direct, well communicated, clear 'I messages.

- 'When you play the music very loudly, I find my space invaded and I feel that I'm not being taken into account.'
- 'When you arrive late for work I have to take up the slack and I feel pressurised.'
- 'When you make decisions without consulting me I feel ignored.'

What does a 'You message' look like? 'You messages' tend

What does a 'You message' look like? 'You messages' tend to be indirect, unclear and bad communication. 'You messages' usually fall into one of the following categories:

- Solution messages, where you strongly suggest how the other person should modify or change **their** behaviour.
- Put-down messages, including judging, blaming, labelling or scapegoating.
- Indirect messages – including sarcasm, teasing or indirect hints.

'You messages' result in ineffective communication, they have a low probability of bringing about the resolution of the problem and often lead to a deterioration of the relationship. 'You messages' don't communicate exactly what is going on or how it affects you. It lays blame for the situation with the other person. You don't take responsibility for your part in creating the situation and you don't show how you have been affected by it.

Examples of 'You messages'
- 'You make me mad or angry.'
- 'You always want things your way.'
- 'You ought to know better.'

Sending 'I messages' can be risky. It involves the risk of self-disclosure; it may involve us looking more closely at our own behaviour and expectations and it encourages us to take responsibility for issues rather than placing the responsibility for them outside ourselves.

People from all backgrounds and of all ages are often quite unaware of how their behaviour and their communication style affects other people. Learning to use 'I messages' can help to change that and can turn thoughtlessness into thoughtfulness as we allow open communication to flow.

Relationship types
Our relationships fall into one of three types:

- Peer relations – where both people involved are equal.

regard to the other person.
- Relationships where you are in a lower position with regard to the other person.

In your relationships, especially where you are in an equally or more powerful position than the other person, you have the choice to move away from 'power over' models of conflict resolutions. In doing so, you not only enhance the quality of your relationships and your own life but you contribute to the creation of world peace. So often when we look at all the conflict in the world we say 'what can I do'? It is encouraging to realise that as each of us find peace within ourselves we actually add to world peace, world peace begins with personal peace!

TEN COMMANDMENTS FOR REDUCING STRESS

1   Thou shalt not be perfect nor even try to be.
2   Thou shalt not try to be all things to all people.
3   Thou shalt leave things undone that ought to be done.
4   Thou shalt not spread thyself too thin.
5   Thou shalt learn to say 'no'.
6   Thou shalt schedule time for thyself and supportive network.
7   Thou shalt switch off and do nothing regularly.
8   Thou shalt be boring, untidy, inelegant and inattentive at times.
9   Thou shalt not ever feel guilty.
10 Especially, thou shalt not be thine own worst enemy but thy best friend.

Author's note: Thou shalt not take life too seriously!

(Thanks to Patricia Ellis who found this on a surgery wall in Brown Bay, New Zealand.)

Epilogue

Beyond stress

Finding peace within yourself, loving and accepting who you are at this moment – moving away from unhealthy guilt and the perfectionism it imposes, and from fear as a guiding principle, is only the beginning of great new possibilities for you and your life.

Confusion and dissatisfaction are great opportunities for change and growth. The development of our true selves requires that we embrace the confusion and anxiety and move through it into a greater experience of our selves and the reality of the universe we inhabit.

All growth and change requires a releasing of what is – sometimes before we know what the actual newness will be – this requires trust in ourselves and the universe.

Do we have any basis for that trust? I believe we do. We live in an interconnected universe. We are part of and sustained by the web of life. Every living thing brings its own unique gifts to the web of life. As each of us reaches our own true potential the web is enhanced and becomes stronger and more beautiful.

May each of us experience the joy of fully creating our unique part of the web.

Useful Addresses

Centres in Ireland

Aisling Arann
An Charraig,
Inis Mhor, Aran Islands,
Co Galway.
Tel: 099-61245

Aisling Centre,
37 Darling St.,
Enniskillen,
Co Fermanagh.
Tel: 0365-325811

**Amethyst, Healing
Therapy & Training
Centre,**
Bray Road, Foxrock,
Dublin 18.
Tel: 01-2893144

**Awakenings Centre for
Human Development &
Healing,**
2 Dodder Park Drive,
Rathfarnham, Dublin 14.
Tel: 01-920122

Beatha Centre,
70 Claremount Rd.,
Circular Rd, Galway,
Co Galway.

**Centre for Biodynamic
Psychology &
Psychotherapy,**
Tracht Beach, Kinvara,
Co Galway.
Tel: 091-37192

**Creative Counselling
Centre,**
86 Pembroke Road,
Dublin 4.
Tel: 01-6683055

Crescent Arts Centre,
2-4 University Rd.,
Belfast,
Co Antrim.
Tel: 0232-243338

Chrysalis,
Donaghmore,
Donard,
Co Wicklow.
Tel: 045-54713

**CJ Jung Society of
Ireland,**
4 Lr. Fitzwilliam St.,
Dublin 2
Tel: 01-767643

Dundalk Counselling Centre,
'Oakdene', Joclyn St.,
Dundalk,
Co Louth.
Tel: 042-38333

Eckhart House,
19 Clyde Road,
Dublin 4.
Tel: 01-6684687

Hanley Centre, Counselling on Alcoholism and Related Issues,
The Mews, Eblana Ave.,
Dun Laoghaire,
Co Dublin.
Tel: 01-2809795

Healing House, Holistic Healing Centre,
24 O'Connell Ave.,
Berkeley Road,
Dublin 7.
Tel: 01-306413

Institute of Integrated Psychotherapy,
26 Longford Tce.,
Monkstown,
Co. Dublin.
Tel: 01-2809313

Iomlánú Centre for Healing & Creative Living,
Roden Place, Dundalk.
Co Louth.
Tel: 042-32804

Irish School of Classical Homeopathy,
28/29 Dame St.,
Dublin 2.

Jampa Ling Tibetan Buddist Centre,
Owendoon,
Bawnboy,
Co Cavan.
Tel: 049-23448

Joan Davis Dance and Movement Studio
330 Harold's Cross,
Dublin 6.

Kiltalown House,
Jobstown,
Tallaght,
Dublin 24.
Tel: 01-522466

'Lifesprings'
111 Clifftonville Road.,
Belfast,
Co Antrim.
Tel: 0232-753658

Lios Dana Natural Living Centre
Inch, Co Kerry.
Tel: 066-58189

Meitheal Community (Residential — Alternative Life Styles),
Inch Pier,
Inch Island,
Co Donegal.
Tel: 077-60323

Natural Living Centre,
Walmer House,
Hilltop,
Raheny,
Dublin 5.
Tel: 01-327859

Sonairte National Ecology Centre,
Laytown,
Co Meath.
Tel: 041-27572

New Birth Centre,
4 Wynnefield Road,
Rathmines,
Dublin 6.
Tel: 01-960948

The Shanty Education Project,
Brittas, Co Dublin.
Tel: 01-510852

Slanú
Galway Healing Centre,
Ballyloughnan Road,
Renmore,
Galway.
Tel: 091-55023

The Source,
11 East Essex St.,
Dublin 2.
Tel: 01-6799915

Turning Point,
23 Crofton Road,
Dun Laoghaire,
Co Dublin.
Tel: 01-2807888

Teach Ban,
Macrobiotic Centre,
6 Parnell Road,
Harolds Cross,
Dublin 6.

Tullycoll House,
10 Tullycoll Road,
Cookstown,
Co Tyrone BF80 9QY.
Tel: 0648-761158

Waymark Centre,
The Rectory,
Daughaustown,
Co Wicklow.
Tel: 0404-47220

Centres in Britain

Alternatives,
St James Church,
Picadilly, London.
Tel: 071-7344811

**Centre for Creation
Spirituality,**
St James Church,
Picadilly,
London.
Tel: 071-734481

Fountain International,
PO Box 52,
Torquay,
Devon TQ2 8PX.

Gaunt House,
Winbourne,
Dorset BH21 4JQ.
Tel: 0202-841522

Monkton Wyld Court,
Chermouth,
Bridport,
Dorset DT6 6DQ.
Tel: 0297-60342

Mysteries,
9-11 Monmouth St.,
Convent Gardens,
London WC2 9DA.
Tel: 071-8364679

The Findhorn Foundation,
The Park,
Forres,
Scotland, IV 36660 RE.
Tel: 0309-672288

The Schumacher College,
Totnes, Devon TQ96EL.
Tel: 0803-865934

Wrekin Trust,
Running Park, Croft Bank,
West Malvern,
Worc. WR14 4BO.
Tel: 0684-892989

International centres

**Atsitsa Skyros Centre and
Skyros Institute, Greece,**
92 Prince of Wales Rd,
London NW5 2NE.
Tel: 071-2843064

Esalen Institute,
Big Sur,
California, Ca 93920.
Tel: 408-667-3000

Feathered Pipe Ranch,
Box 1682,
Helena,
Montana 59624.
Tel: 406-442-8196

**Institute for Creation
Sprituality,**
Holy Names College,
3500 Mountain Blvd.,
Oakland Ca 94619.
Tel: 510-436-1046

**Peace Through
Understanding,**
PO Box 95910, NL-2509,
CX Den Haag, Holland.
Tel: 31-20-6244999

Further reading and references

Adams, Linda with Leny, Elinor. *Effectiveness Training for Women.* New York: Putnains, 1979.

Baker, Lynn, Cooper, C l and Cooper R D. *Living with Stress.* Middlesex, Penguin Health, 1988.

Borysenko, Joan. *Guilt is the Teacher, Love is the Answer.* New York: Crucible Books, 1990.

Borysenko, Joan. *Minding the Body, Mending the Mind.* London: Bantam, 1988.

Bradshaw, John. *Healing the Shame that Binds You.* Florida: Health Communications Inc, 1988.

Brawn, Barbary B. *Between Health and Illness.* New York: Bantam, 1985.

Brennan, Barbara Ann. *Hands of Light.* New York: Bantam, 1987.

Browne, Molly. *The Unfolding Self.* California: Psychosynthesis Press, 1983.

Burns, David. *The Feeling Good Handbook.* New York: Plume-Penguin, 1990.

Campbell, Peter and McMahon, Edwin. *Biospirituality: Focusing as a Way to Grow.* Chicago: Loyola University Press, 1985.

Crum, Thomas F. *The Magic of Conflict.* London: Touchstone, Simon & Schuster, 1987.

Dickson, Anne. *A Woman in Her Own Right.* London: Touchstone, Simon & Schuster, 1983.

Dickson, Anne. *The Mirror Within.* London: Quartet Books, 1985.

Dowling, George. *The Book of Massage.* New York: Random House, 1972.

Dyer, Wayne. *Your Erroneous Zones.* London: Sphere Books, 1977.

Ferruci, P. *What We May Be.* Los Angeles: Tarcher, 1976.

Fox, Matthew. *Creation Spirituality,* San Francisco: Harper, 1991.

Fox, Matthew. *Original Blessing.* Santa Fe, New Mexico: Bear & Co, 1983.

Freeman, Andrea and Gray, Harry. *Teaching Without Stress.* London: Chapman, 1988.

Gawain, Shakti. *Creative Visualisation.* California: New World Library. 1978.

Gendlin, Eugene. *Focusing.* New York: Bantam, 1981.

Gordon, Dr Thomas. *Teacher Effectiveness Training.* New York: Peter Wyden, 1974.

Grant, Mary et al. *Aromatheraphy Workbook.* Belfast: Lifesprings Centre, 1992.

Hay, Louise. *You Can Heal Your Life.* London: Eden Grove Publications, 1984.

Hay, Louise. *The Power Within.* London: Eden Grove Publications, 1991.

Hendricks, Gay, Hendricks, Kathlyn. *Conscious Loving.* New York: Bantam, 1992.

Houston, Jean, and Masters, Robert. *Listening to the Body.* Delaconte: New York, 1978.

Houston, Jean. *The Possible Human.* Los Angeles: J P Tarcher, 1982.

Krista, Alix. *The Book of Stress Survival.* London: Unwin Books, 1986.

Levy, Joel. *Fine Arts of Relaxation, Concentration and Meditation.* London: Wisdom Books, 1987.

Livington-Booth, Dr Audrey. *Less Stress and More Success.* London: Severn House, 1988.

Marichild, Diana. *Mother Wit.* California: The Crossing Press, 1981

Marichild, Diana. *Inner Dance.* California: The Crossing Press, 1984.

Markham, Ursula. *Managing Stress.* Dorset: Element Books, 1989.

Mason, John L. *Guide to Stress Reduction.* Berkeley, California: Celestial Arts, 1985.

Murdocks, Maureen. *The Heroine's Journey.* Berkeley, California: Shambhala, 1990.

Neylon, Margaret. *Pathways.* Dublin: Attic Press, 1991.

Padovani, Martin H. *Healing Wounded Emotions.* Connetticut: Mystic, 1987.

Paulus, Trina. *Hope for the Flowers.* New York: Paullist Press, 1972.

Pinkola Estes, Clarissa. *Women who Run with the Wolves.* New York: Ballintine Books, 1992.

Price, Shirley. *Aromatherapy for Common Ailments.* London: Gaia Books, 1991

Pronto, Louis. *Self Healing.* London: Piatkus, 1990.

Satir, Virginia. *Peoplemaking.* London: Souvenir Press, 1978.

Schierese Leonard, Linda. *On the Way to the Wedding,* California: Shambhala, 1986.

Segal, Jeanne. *Living Beyond Fear.* California: Newcastle Publications, 1987.

Shaprio, Debbie. *The Bodymind Book.* Dorset: Element Books, 1990.

Smith, M J. *When I Say No I Feel Guilty.* New York: Bantam, 1975.

Tisserand, Robert. *The Art of Aromatherapy.* Essex: C W Daniel, 1977.

Whitworth, Diana. *Psychosynthesis in Education.* Wellingboro: Turnstone Press, 1986.

Worwood, Valerie Ann. *The Fragrant Pharmacy.* New York: Bantam, 1991.

Whelan, Dolores. *Waves of Relaxation* (tape). Dundalk: Iómlanú Books, 1988.

Index

141

142